Tots About Town

The NCT Baby and Toddler Guide to Guildford

Produced by Carla Applegate and Gemma Gregson

First published in 2002 by Guildford NCT

This new revised edition published 2013

Copyright ©2013, 2007, 2002 Guildford NCT
c/o Alexandra House, Oldham Terrace, London, W3 6NH
guildfordtotsabouttown@gmail.com
www.nct.org.uk/branches/guildford

The moral right of the authors has been asserted.

The views and opinions expressed in this publication are not necessarily those of the NCT.

A CIP catalogue record for this book is available from the British Library.

ISBN 978-0-9541840-2-5

Produced in association with the NCT
Registered office: Alexandra House, Oldham Terrace, London, W3 6NH
www.nct.org.uk
Registered charity no: 801395
Registered company no: 2370573

Typeset by Shore Books and Design
Printed and bound in Great Britain by
TJ International, Padstow, Cornwall, PL28 8RW

A Note from the Editors

When considering what we wanted from the new edition, we decided it was the reviews that were the main attraction. There is something very special about the reviews which really grab at what is important to us as parents about the places we go and the things we do with our little ones. While everyone wants slightly different things for their children, we all want them to have fun and be happy.

To our minds, it is the personal touch which is the great thing about a review book; someone has gone to the trouble of putting pen to paper to pass on the information for the benefit of other parents. With that in mind, we have stuck to including, in the main, just the details for those places we have received reviews for. We are incredibly lucky to live in an area where there are so many great things going on for children, and there are many more out there. Of course, all the reviews are individual to the reviewers and do not necessarily represent the views of the NCT.

While we have taken great care to ensure that address information and times are correct, things do change and we cannot guarantee their accuracy. Especially with babies and toddlers strapped in the buggy or back of the car, it is always a good idea to double-check before setting off anywhere. We have included web addresses where possible to allow you to research the activities, attractions and outlets.

The advertisers in this book were approached on the basis that they have services or facilities that are in keeping with the information in this book. However, having an advert in the book does not constitute endorsement by the NCT of the advertiser, although all comply with the advertising standards and ethics set by the NCT.

We very much hope you enjoy this all-new edition of *Tots About Town* and that it brings you and your little ones many happy days and lots and lots of fun.

Carla Applegate and Gemma Gregson

Contents

Introduction

Carla Applegate, mum to Ellis
Gemma Gregson, mum to Daniel

We are delighted to welcome you to the third edition of *Tots About Town*.

This edition would never have got off the ground if we had not been so inspired by the previous editions. Once we started working on the project, it soon became clear that there were a lot of people who were also very excited about seeing a new edition of their much-loved book and so our team assembled, reviews came in and, finally, the presses were rolling. With only our love of *Tots About Town* as any kind of relevant experience, we were very lucky to meet some lovely people willing to share the wealth of their knowledge, time and enthusiasm. Please read our acknowledgements page at the back of the book for our special thank yous to all who have been part of this edition.

We both found the previous edition of *Tots About Town* invaluable with our children. The idea of a review book appeals on so many levels. Sharing knowledge is all part of the parenting process and part of the joy of *Tots About Town* is feeling part of that. And when we go somewhere we have read about in *Tots About Town*, we have a much better idea of what to expect, some insider tips and above all, a recommendation that there is fun to be had. As children inevitably change, grow and develop new skills, there are new activities for them to try and *Tots About Town* is there to tell you all about them.

It was very clear that the time was ripe for a fully revised edition. For the last few years, new members have been told that there is a new edition coming soon(!), those who did such a great job last time are now firmly on the school run, and there are always new places opening and something new to try!

We have absolutely loved the challenge of putting this edition together. It has certainly been something totally different to our usual sphere of activity! Like all good babies, it has kept us awake at night, taken up more time than we could ever have imagined, but has also brought us incredible joy and we are proud of what we have produced. We hope that our enthusiasm has brought you a new edition to enjoy for many years to come.

1. All About the NCT
Katie Kelly, mum to Beth and Asa

What is the NCT?
0300 330 0770
www.nct.org.uk

The NCT is a national charity that aims to support parents during their child's early years by offering information and support in pregnancy, birth and early parenthood. The charity is currently particularly focused on increasing the number of people who can access its support and services, with the aim of reaching 20 million parents by 2020.

It is also a major campaigner for improved maternity care and services for new parents. The NCT provides easy access to evidence-based information via the website, e-newsletters, helplines, courses, magazines and other publications.

NCT Antenatal Teachers, *Breastfeeding Counsellors* and Postnatal Leaders train for an average of three years before they start taking groups and their qualifications are accredited not only by the NCT but also by the University of Bedford and the University of Worcester.

NCT Guildford
www.nct.org.uk/branches/guildford
www.facebook.com/nctguildford

The charity has a nationwide network of local branches and the Guildford branch provides a great range of services and activities for parents, from *Antenatal Courses* to *Bumps and Babes* meet-ups and baby and toddler swims at the *Spectrum*. Visit the Guildford pages of the NCT website or NCT Guildford on Facebook to find out what's happening now.

Classes and Courses
0844 243 6917
bookings4l@nct.org.uk
www.nct.org.uk/branches/guildford/courses

Antenatal Courses
Katie Kelly, NCT Antenatal Teacher, mum to Beth and Asa

These come in a range of formats including one evening a week for eight weeks and all-day courses run at weekends. These courses are not only a fantastic opportunity to have all your questions about labour, birth and life with a new baby answered, but they are also an amazing way to meet people who will know exactly what you are going through because they are experiencing it too. These courses incorporate a breastfeeding session with an NCT *Breastfeeding Counsellor* to give you plenty of information about feeding your baby once it arrives.

In addition, the branch also runs one-off labour days and waterbirth workshops for those who would like to look at these specific issues in more detail.

'My husband and I attended one of the NCT *Antenatal Courses* when I was pregnant with my first child. I had read most books cover to cover, my husband hadn't read so much as a blurb. The course was ideal for both of us. It forced my husband to face the reality of the birth and what could and might happen. For me, I got answers to all of my 101 questions.
Furthermore, we met a brilliant group of people who formed the basis of our baby network. To such an extent that three years later, we've all gone back to work, but have the same days off. We've been on holiday together and all had second children and supported each other through this as well. You can meet a number of mums through different groups, but the way the NCT courses are run mean you can really meet new friends for life, which when you're relocating (I'd moved to Guildford from London) is priceless.
The teachers are well informed, relaxed and happy to support you with any questions or problems you might be worried about. Worth every penny.'
Shelley, mum to Harriet and Hugo

'For me, the classes were great for two main reasons. Firstly, for learning what to expect from labour and the immediate aftermath; understanding exactly what is going on 'in there' in terms of hormones and what your body is doing. And also knowing what your choices are in labour, so that when the midwives say something, you understand what it means and don't freak out, and you also understand that you have a right to question them – it is *your* labour after

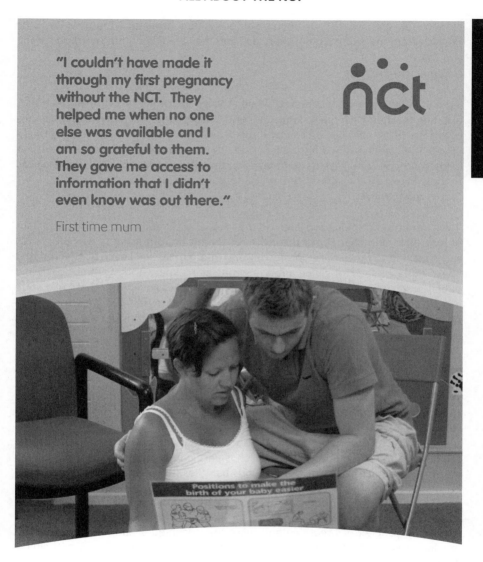

"I couldn't have made it through my first pregnancy without the NCT. They helped me when no one else was available and I am so grateful to them. They gave me access to information that I didn't even know was out there."

First time mum

Positions to make the birth of your baby easier

89% of mothers-to-be said they felt more confident about giving birth following an NCT Antenatal Class.

all. Secondly, the classes have been great for meeting other local mums-to-be. I see the girls from my group almost every day and they are a continued support for me and Max.'
Georgie, mum to Max

'I didn't know quite what to expect when I turned up for my NCT *Antenatal Course*, but the teacher was really kind and enthusiastic and not only answered any questions that I had, but also helped me answer questions I hadn't even thought of yet! The classes helped my partner and I to work out what we wanted from our birth experience and gave us confidence when talking to the midwives. It was hard to drag myself off the sofa at 7pm on a Tuesday night, but it was worth it.'
Carrie, mum to Eve

'I will admit to not being too keen on the idea of antenatal classes. I pictured a lot of joss sticks and chat about the cycles of the moon, but in fact I was pleasantly surprised. I found the course interesting and informative and I even discovered that I have quite a knack for giving a relaxing massage. I knew nothing about birth and babies when we started, but by the time the course was over I felt that I had quite a good understanding of what to expect. I even found myself doing extra research on the internet and now, with a second child on the way, I consider myself quite an expert!'
Al, dad to Nicholas and bump

Antenatal Refresher Courses
Terri Walter, NCT Antenatal Teacher and Relax, Stretch and Breathe Teacher, mum to Ben, Chloe and Philippa

Joining an NCT *Refresher Course* is a great way to meet other women with babies due around the same time as you, which is particularly helpful if you have moved into the area since you had your previous baby/ies. However, there is much more on offer than that. The courses are facilitated by an NCT Antenatal Teacher and give you the opportunity to discuss your past birth experiences, update yourself with changes in birth policy and research findings since your last birth as well as reminding yourself of breathing and relaxation techniques and, very importantly, looking at issues such as integrating your new baby into your family and sibling rivalry.

'The course was great in giving me time out of my busy life to focus on this baby and imminent birth. Good discussions on life with two and nice to meet other mums about to go through the same thing.'
Karen, mum to Jodie

ALL ABOUT THE NCT

'I didn't get the opportunity to do an NCT antenatal class with my first child and found myself envious of the groups of new mums that I saw in cafés. When we moved to Guildford and I found I was pregnant I didn't want to miss out again so I booked my *Refresher Course*. I'm so glad I did and the seven mums I met are now firm friends.

Terri led the group, rather than 'teaching' us, which was great. The emphasis was on sharing our experiences, and I came away with a wealth of knowledge from the other ladies' previous births (and their secondhand stories as well). Terri's information gave me enormous insight into the things I considered to have 'gone wrong' in my first birth, and enabled me to research and plan for a much more relaxed and controlled second birth. Discussion and learning were interspersed with lots of breathing exercises, visualisations and practice 'contractions', skills that were invaluable in helping me achieve a pain-relief free birth.'
Katie, mum to Sebastian and Alexander

Early Days Courses
Catherine Wands, NCT Postnatal Leader and Relax and Stretch with Baby Teacher, mum to Elisabeth, William and Emma

Becoming a parent is one of the most exciting and amazing things you'll ever do. It's also often the case that the first few months can be bewildering and exhausting. It's easy to feel isolated and that everyone else knows more about parenting than you do. *Early Days Courses* are designed to give you greater confidence in facing the challenges of motherhood. You'll have the chance to come together with other new mothers from Guildford to share experiences, pick up some useful information and coping strategies and find out that you are not the only one feeling the way you do. Of course, it's also a wonderful opportunity to celebrate all the good things about being a mother.

These weekly postnatal courses are usually five sessions long and are for mothers with babies up to six months. They run throughout the year.

First Aid Courses
These invaluable courses are taught by the Red Cross and are run as morning or afternoon sessions.
www.nct.org.uk/branches/events/baby-first-aid

'When Ellis was tiny, a big worry was about his health in general and whether I'd know what to do in an emergency. Then as he got bigger, there were new dangers that came with him starting solids and being able to move around and fall over (all the time!). This class was great to reassure me that, although he would become ill

5

or bang his head from time to time, I would have some knowledge to help him as much as possible should anything happen to him. It was an excellent course, I learnt a lot, and was able to take baby along with me so it was really easy too.'
Carla, mum to Ellis

Introducing Solids Workshops
Claire Boud, NCT Postnatal Leader, mum to Callum, Sophie and Toby

Introducing solid foods to your baby can be an exciting and nerve-wracking (not to mention messy) time. Many parents become confused by conflicting advice and concerned that their baby is getting enough food. These discussion-based two-hour workshops, led by an NCT Postnatal Leader may cover topics such as when to introduce solids, purées, baby-led weaning and what foods to avoid.

The courses are designed for parents and carers and their babies. It doesn't matter if you have already started giving your baby solids, or if your baby is breastfed or bottle-fed.

'I went on the NCT one day weaning course that cost £25. It was a small group so you didn't feel silly asking questions and the lady running it was brilliant.'
Miriam, mum to Caitlin

Swimming – Tadpoles
Shelley Collinson, NCT Guildford Chair, mum to Harriet and Hugo

Tadpoles is an unstructured swimming session that runs every Thursday during term time from 10.30am-12pm. It is held in the baby pool at *Guildford Spectrum*. Anne, who has been running the sessions for years, is always poolside to help, either with getting in and out the pool or offering advice for getting the babies to kick or splash. The session really wouldn't be the same without her. There are plenty of toys in the pool, armbands at the side and a number of baby changing mats. Tickets for the session can either be bought on a one-off basis or in books of five or ten. This means once you've bought your ticket you can go on the weeks that suit you and you don't pay for weeks you can't attend.

Guildford Spectrum, Parkway, GU1 1UP
07850 025880
nctswimenquiry@live.co.uk
www.nct.org.uk/branches/guildford/events/baby-swimming/8
(Also see *Tadpoles* on page 60)

'This is such a bargain. When we have been to public pools, it has cost nearly £15 for all three of us to swim. With the NCT swimming, you are paying just a few pounds a time, and you pay per child. Lots of toys and a lovely helpful instructor if you're ever at a loss as to what to do with your little one in the pool.'
Carla, mum to Ellis

Prenatal and Postnatal Exercise
www.nct.org.uk/branches/guildford/courses

Relax, Stretch and Breathe and Yoga for Pregnancy classes
Terri Walters, NCT Antenatal Teacher and Relax, Stretch and Breathe Teacher, mum to Ben, Chloe and Philippa

The NCT has developed its own classes for pregnant women that use gentle yoga postures, breathing techniques and relaxation combined with positions for labour to help prepare the body for birth. Both *Relax, Stretch and Breathe* classes and *Yoga for Pregnancy* can help reduce the aches and pains of pregnancy and improve quality of sleep, as well as posture and body awareness. Setting aside this time to focus on your body and your baby can help you bond with your unborn baby as well as increase your confidence in your ability to cope with the labour and birth. These classes run on a pay-as-you-go basis and are open to members and non-members alike. Concessionary rates are available.

'The skills I learnt at *Relax, Stretch and Breathe* absolutely helped. I was intending to have a mobile epidural for my birth. As it happened, the first stage of labour happened so quickly that there wasn't time for an epidural, so I relied purely on the breathing techniques and focusing exercises learnt in the classes. Remaining calm helped me deal with the pain of each contraction.
I would highly recommend this class, in fact it was so relaxing that on several occasions I got a full night's sleep once I got home. There was a great balance of exercises and relaxation and also a chance to meet and talk to other mums-to-be. At the end of each class we were given a drink and a biscuit which is a lovely touch and a great way to end the session sharing a few minutes talking to the person on the next mat.'
Amanda, mum to Rufus

'I do think *Relax, Stretch and Breathe* helped me, if only to keep me doing deep breathing throughout labour - in fact afterwards the doctor asked me if I did yoga as they were very impressed with how focused I stayed on my breathing throughout a difficult and intense labour! Great class – would sign up much earlier in pregnancy if I become pregnant with number two sometime in the future.'
Alisar, mum to Ronan

'These classes are designed to help you relax, stretch and breathe in the final months of pregnancy and they do just that. I used to love my regular time to switch off, focus on my bump and think about the birth. I found it a really practical and enjoyable class and the practice contractions I found strange but actually really helpful once they were happening for real! Terri is a great instructor and instigates useful conversations to get us all chatting and thinking about labour, but in a calm way. I missed the class once I had my baby and had to join another yoga class straight away!'
Claire, mum to Orson

Relax and Stretch with Baby
Catherine Wands, NCT Postnatal Leader and Relax and Stretch with Baby Teacher, mum to Elisabeth, William and Emma

These yoga-inspired exercise sessions, led by an NCT Postnatal Leader, are for mums and babies and are designed to help you feel stronger and more confident about your body after birth as well as to help stimulate your baby's development through movement and play. There's also time to share a little post-exercise refreshment and talk to other mothers. Suitable for women who have had their six to eight week postnatal check-up.

Services

Bra Fitting Service
Nickkie Elms, NCT Antenatal Teacher and Bra Fitter, mum to Katie and Alice

The Guildford NCT branch offers a free and friendly maternity/nursing bra service. This is available to NCT members and non-members alike. Individual fittings take place at the bra fitter's house, alternatively larger groups sometimes arrange a 'Beer and Bra Night', which entails all the mums-to-be getting fitted while the dads-to-be get some time down the local pub. A fun night for all!
nctguildfordbras@gmail.com

'Having struggled through my pregnancy with a variety of ill-fitting, uncomfortable bras I decided that I needed someone who understood the (dramatic) changes that happen to a woman's breasts when breastfeeding and I didn't think I could face struggling into bras in a shop changing room while my newborn daughter announced her boredom to the world.
So, I went to see the Guildford NCT bra fitter. She was fantastic and put me at my ease so I didn't feel at all embarrassed trying the bras. The bra she recommended

fitted perfectly and was possibly the most comfortable bra I have ever had. An antenatal teacher with young children of her own, the fitter was completely unfazed by my daughter's yelling, and being in someone's home made it a really relaxed experience.'

Kate, mum to Banjo and Elvie

Breastfeeding Counsellors
Amy Carter, Student NCT Breastfeeding Counsellor, mum to Thomas and Oliver

NCT Helpline 0300 330 0771
Or contact them via the branch or a *Bosom Buddies* meet up (see page 13)

NCT *Breastfeeding Counsellors* are all mothers who have breastfed their babies. They know how worthwhile and enjoyable breastfeeding can be but are also aware of the help and support that many new mothers need. After completing a university level qualification, they work – mainly voluntarily through the NCT – to support mothers.

Breastfeeding Counsellors can support a woman during pregnancy and at any time during her breastfeeding journey. They are also available to provide support and information to other members of a woman's family.

Breastfeeding Counsellors help women to talk through their concerns, whether large or small, and to feel comfortable with breastfeeding. They are mother-centred in their attitudes to baby feeding, and positive and supportive to all mothers; their role is not to advise or tell a mother what to do. It is rather to be of help in building a mother's confidence in her own ability to cope and to enable her to make her own decisions with the benefit of evidence-based information.

You can ask a *Breastfeeding Counsellor* about anything you have questions or worries about with regard to feeding your baby! For example your feelings about breastfeeding, concerns about milk supply, nipple and breast pain, wondering if something is normal, returning to work, expressing, combination feeding, introducing solids and stopping breastfeeding.

Breastfeeding Counsellors are not qualified to deal with medical issues but will be able to help you decide whether you need to visit your health professional and can offer self-help measures in the meantime.

They can be contacted on the national helpline and the Guildford Branch also has local *Breastfeeding Counsellors* available.

ALL ABOUT THE NCT

Breast Pump Hire
0844 243 6145

You can hire an electric breast pump from the NCT. These are particularly useful for helping you to breastfeed premature or sick babies.

Library

We have a small collection of books on pregnancy, birth and parenting available for loan. The *library* is held at *G Live* and is accessible to members at the monthly coffee mornings with *busylizzy* (see page 14).

Nearly New Sales
www.nct.org.uk/branches/guildford/nearly-new-sales

'As a mother of two (soon to be three) children I completely love and rely on the NCT *Nearly New Sales* to clothe and toy my children for the six to twelve months ahead. They run like a shop – albeit the busiest one you have ever been to – whereby you speed around looking, deciding and then bagging all the items on your wish list in about an hour and a half. As it is a nearly new sale, toys, equipment and clothes are all of a good standard and if you ever have any problems then the team that run the sale try their best to help you out. You can find most things that you need at the sale from moses baskets to wellies, books to snow suits. If you can buy it in a shop then you are bound to find at least one of it at a *Nearly New Sale*. The sales tend to run three times a year and you can always find out more info about them on the NCT website.'
Rebecca, mum to Isobel and George

Newsletter
Katie Le Vallee, newsletter editor, mum to Sebastian and Alexander

The *newsletter* is a one-stop-shop for members, and a nice, easy read over a precious cup of tea when everything goes quiet for a minute! Produced quarterly, it contains themed articles on a variety of topics relevant to pregnancy, babies and young children (recent themes have included homebirths, surviving summer with babies and young children and babies on a budget). Regular features include Dad's Digest, the breastfeeding pages, Meet the Member and Your NCT, which introduces readers to one of the many regular events that go on in the area. There is NCT branch and national news and it is a great first stop in finding out how you can get more involved, either through courses and services, coffee mornings or even *volunteering*.

The *newsletter* is also a valuable point of reference, containing contact details for your local NCT committee as well as local support services, and information on regular and upcoming events such as coffee mornings, fundraisers, *Nearly New Sales*, swimming and more.

Pregnancy and Birth Helpline
0300 330 0772

Call and speak to an antenatal teacher about any questions or issues you have about pregnancy and birth, or just to chat about your experiences.

Shared Experiences Helpline
0300 330 0774

If you are having difficulties connected with pregnancy, birth and the early years, you are not alone and it might help to talk to someone who has had the same experience and got through it. The NCT *Shared Experiences Helpline* can be a wonderful source of support, putting you in touch with someone who can really understand what you are going through.

Valley Cushion Hire
0844 243 6145

The *Valley Cushion* is specially designed to relieve pressure when sitting, and can be invaluable if stitches, tears, bruising or haemorrhoids are causing you discomfort. The branch has one for hire.

Volunteering

'I decided to help out with the Guildford *Nearly New Sale* when my little girl was four months old. I'd met some great people through our NCT antenatal classes and just wanted to give something back. After helping at two of the sales I realised how few volunteers there actually were and how it was a really nice group to be part of. I started to help out a little more and after a few months the Treasurer announced that she was moving to Dubai. I'm an accountant and know how much other people hate being involved with numbers, so I decided to take the plunge. For me it's been a great way to expand my baby network and get to know more mums locally. It's also kept me sane through two rounds of maternity leave, with some adult company and excuses to leave the house, even if it is only for a committee meeting. Please join us, we need more volunteers!'
Shelley Collinson, NCT Guildford Chair, mum to Harriet and Hugo

'*Volunteering* gives me a chance to use my brain again. It gives me a sense of pride that I am helping people by offering a free service that I could have really benefited from when I was a new mum. It also provides my children (five and eight) with a good example of the fact that in life we should help others.'
Nickkie Elms, NCT Antenatal Teacher and Bra Fitter, mum to Katie and Alice

Social

From regular *Bumps and Babes* meet ups to pub nights and summer and Christmas parties, there is always something going on that offers you a chance to meet other parents and to have a good time with the friends you have already made. And, of course, if it's not there and you would like it to be, get in touch – maybe you can set something up yourself!

One of the best places to check for details of social events is the branch Facebook page: *www.facebook.com/nctguildford*

Bosom Buddies
All Saints Church Reading Room, Vicarage Gate, GU2 7QJ

Bosom Buddies is a friendly social group for mothers who are breastfeeding babies of any age. Both members and non-members are welcome and siblings can go along too. There is free parking next to the hall.

Bumps and Babes
The Trinity Centre, GU1 3RR

'*Bumps and Babes* group is a great way to meet other mums-to-be and new parents of babies up to about seven months old. Mums can have a chat and a coffee while the babies play on the play mats provided. This group was very welcoming and was the highlight of the week for both my husband and me in our daughter's early months.'
Femke, mum to Stephanie

'I found this a lovely group, especially in the early days. Kind support from the NCT and all the other new mums when you are wondering if it's just you! Cup of tea made for you and play mats for the babies. Great for small babies without worrying about older ones running around.'
Carla, mum to Ellis

'*Bumps and Babes* saved my sanity when, at 41 weeks pregnant, I was still waiting

for Isabelle to arrive. Once she was born it was a brilliant support network. One that all new (and old) mums need.'
Katy, mum to Isabelle

Coffee Morning with busylizzy
G Live, London Road, GU1 2AA

This relaxed, friendly meet is held on the second Tuesday of every month in the café at *G Live* (see page 133).

Mums of Two or More
Castle Nursery, Old School Close, GU1 4QJ

Monthly coffee morning for those with two (or more!), held on the first Friday of the month. See Facebook for more details: *www.facebook.com/nctguildford*

2. Days Out
Tracy Liennard, mum to Eliza and Wilfred

The arrival of children in your life brings many changes, for me one of the biggest was no longer having my days decided by work, or which friends I was seeing at the weekends. I found I had five days a week, and sometimes another day at the weekend if daddy was playing sport, to fill with interesting and engaging activities for both my child and myself. Luckily Guildford and the surrounding area have a wealth of interesting places to visit to keep your children happy and yourself sane. In this area we are lucky enough to have some of the best places to visit in the UK.

Aquariums, Bird Parks and Zoos

Birdworld
Holt Pound, Farnham, GU10 4LD
01420 22992
www.birdworld.co.uk

'As the name suggests, there are lots of different types of birds to see. They also have various events on throughout the day such as penguin feeding and an outdoor flying display. As well as all the birds, there is a children's farm and Underwater World. My son loved watching all the different types of fish and seeing the crocodiles. There is a range of eating options or you can take your own picnic. It is easy to get around with a pushchair and there are play areas for when the little ones want to take a break from the buggy and run off some steam.'
Gemma, mum to Daniel

Blue Reef Aquarium
Clarence Esplanade, Southsea, Hampshire, PO5 3PB
023 9287 5222
www.bluereefaquarium.co.uk

'Babies love watching the brightly coloured fish and older children will appreciate all the different varieties and feeding time! There are changing facilities and a small café is attached. A walk along the stony beach afterwards, throwing stones in the sea, should ensure a peaceful trip home.'
Carla, mum to Ellis

Drusillas Park
Alfriston, East Sussex, BN26 5QS
01323 874100
www.drusillas.co.uk

'We visited in September 2011 and had a fun day. It is mainly suitable for younger children and toddlers. Their focus is on interaction. Around every corner is something for the children (and adults too!) to look at, see and read. My son particularly liked all the small mammals, with the prairie dogs being a particular hit! He also liked walking through some of the enclosures and getting up close and personal with the birds and bats! The highlight of the day was the ride on the Thomas the Tank engine train which was great fun.
We took our own picnic with us but it was very busy and we struggled to find somewhere to eat it as all the picnic benches were full. My top tip (which we realised at the exit!) is to have your picnic just outside the zoo – there is a little playground and picnic benches and it was empty! You just have to stamp your own hand to re-enter the park when you're done – easy! The zoo is super child-friendly – the toilets are great, child sized loos and hand basins and even child loo seats that are attached to the loos! They also had a book that you can spot all the animals as you go round and stamp your little book – this seemed very popular with the children. A great little zoo! Would definitely recommend!'
Victoria, mum to Freddy

'*Drusillas* is regularly voted one of the best family attractions in the South East and rightly so. We had a fantastic day out here last summer with our three and one-year-olds. This place is designed with small children in mind – everything is at their eye-level. It is the perfect size for little legs – not too far to walk. The usual zoo animal trail is brought to life with fun facts (try the 'Zoolympics') and animal passport stamping stations – each child has a passport to fill with animal stamps on the way round (ours loved this added novelty!). Well laid out and with a fabulous adventure play area at the end where you could easily spend a couple of hours – lots to entertain kids of all ages. There is also a sizeable soft play zone should the weather prove unfriendly. One of the best family days out we've had. We got our tickets with Tesco Clubcard vouchers – so great value too!'
Ruth, mum to George and William

DAYS OUT

Hawk Conservancy Trust
Sarson Lane, Weyhill, Andover, Hampshire, SP11 8DY
01264 773850
www.hawk-conservancy.org

'Definitely worth the journey if your pre-schooler is interested in owls, vultures, hawks, eagles and the like. The flying displays are amazing, with huge birds of prey swooping low over the heads of the audience. There are plenty of good scampering opportunities for those with difficulty sitting still. Nice restaurant and fun shop, small picnic area.'
Katie, mum to Beth and Asa

Marwell Wildlife
Thompsons Lane, Colden Common, Winchester, Hampshire, SO21 1JH
01962 777407
www.marwell.org.uk

'*Marwell Zoo* is somewhere we love to come. We have been quite a few times and it never disappoints. The zoo is set in huge, beautiful grounds and is really good for walking around. It is very pram-friendly and everywhere has ramps but generally the park is flat. The animals seem to have really big enclosures which is good and there is a wide variety of animals there. The penguins were definitely a favourite with our child. Watching the rhinos fight was a real treat and you can get up close and personal with the giraffes in their 'house'. There is a reptile house and a petting zoo so it really does have a wide variety of things to do – definitely worth going early to fit it all in!
We have eaten in their restaurant but beware – it does get really busy. They could do with opening a new one! We have also taken a picnic with us as there are loads of places on the grass or picnic tables. The toilets and baby change are not that clean and could do with a re-vamp but this is my only complaint! We always look forward to coming here and we love it so much we even looked into hiring the stunning Marwell House - situated in the middle of the grounds for a christening (we didn't in the end as it was rather pricey!)'
Victoria, mum to Freddy

'Entrance is quite pricey (although under-threes are free) so for value for money, and given the distance to get there, this is definitely one to do when you have a whole day free. The park is huge, and there are lots of things to see with pretty much any animal you can think of (ok, there are no Ligers!). You can get a slight discount and priority entrance if you book online beforehand. The park itself is big enough that as well as the ride-on train (at additional cost) there is a free road train to get around the park for those who aren't so keen on walking.'
Andy, dad to Matthew

Farms

Bocketts Farm
Young Street, Fetcham, Leatherhead, KT22 9BS
01372 363764
www.bockettsfarm.co.uk

'There really is a lot to do here, and not only have we taken Matthew (when about nine months), but also his older cousins (aged up to ten). As well as the usual variety of farm animals, time it right in spring and there is lambing to watch. They also have the regular daily pig racing. There are indoor and outdoor play areas, tractor and trailer rides and animal handling sessions.'
Debbie, mum to Matthew, and auntie to Megan, Jessie and Daniel

'The children love it here. There are lots of animals to see and lots of play areas too. The highlight is pig racing which takes place twice a day.'
Louise, mum to Joe, Emilia and Sam

Finkley Down Farm
Andover, Hampshire, SP11 6NF
01264 324141
www.finkleydownfarm.co.uk

'This is a really lovely farm in Andover. It took around an hour to get to but was well worth the journey. It has lots for all ages but is particularly good for toddlers. There are outdoor playgrounds, lots of animals to feed, a nice café, a sand pit and a go-kart area. If the weather turns bad while you are there, the farm has two soft play areas, one for small toddlers and also a large indoor soft play area similar in size and set-up to *Rokers Little Angels* (see pages 66 and 112). It was not badly priced for what you get and you can spend a whole day here. It felt really safe and I was comfortable for my inquisitive toddler to wander much further from me than I have been at other locations.'
Tracy, mum to Eliza and Wilfred

Fishers Farm Park
Newpound Lane, Wisborough Green, West Sussex, RH14 0EG
01403 700063
www.fishersfarmpark.co.uk

'There is so much to do here, including soft play, tractor rides, water splash areas, climbing walls, jumping pillows, sand pits, barrel bug rides and seeing farm animals!

A lovely day for children up to say 12 years old. The entry price may seem a little steep but it is a really enjoyable day out.

My personal favourite activities were the barrel ride (beware: they are easy enough to get into but rather awkward to clamber out of!) and jumping on the giant pillows. There is also a zip wire with a toddler swing chair attached, so your toddler can have a go on the zip wire years before they are able to do the more grown-up ones – this was a great favourite with my two-year-old. It is pricey so get your money's worth by spending the whole day here.'

Tara, mum to Elliott

Garsons

Winterdown Road, West End, Esher, KT10 8LS
01372 464389
www.garsons.co.uk/c/pyo-farm

'A great way to teach children where fruit and veg come from while having a fun day out – as my son says "It's better than Tesco's". *Garsons* has a huge variety of fruit and veg and the prices are ok (availability and price lists are on the website). You can drive between the fields and there is space for picnics. Attached is also a garden centre (which has a small playground) and farm shop.'

Leigh, mum to Ries and Elsa

Godstone Farm

Tilburstow Hill Road, Godstone, RH9 8LX
01883 742546
www.godstonefarm.co.uk

'One of my absolute favourite family days out as there is so much to do! Amble freely around the fully stocked farm, enjoy something in the café, play in a huge soft play with a fabulous toddler section, or sit and enjoy one of the large outdoor play parks and sand pits which are full of a great selection of trucks, spades and buckets! Even when it's busy there's plenty of room for everyone as it's huge!'

Nickkie, mum to Katie and Alice

Hobbledown

Horton Lane, Epsom, KT19 8PT
0843 289 4979
www.hobbledown.com

'This has recently been refurbished and reopened as *Hobbledown* (previously Horton Park Farm). Although we haven't been, we have heard that it is now an excellent place to go.'

Louise, mum to Joe, Emilia and Sam

Ladyland Farm
Meath Green Lane, Horley, RH6 8JA
01293 784469
www.ladylandfarm.com

'If you fancy travelling a bit further then this is a real find. It's only open during August weekdays starting at 11am and closing at 3pm. Ideally it would suit older toddlers and children, but it's a great structured day out with lots of information and chance for the kids to get hands on with feeding and touching the animals. The day starts at 11am by the farm house (plenty of parking and no need to book) – bring a pack lunch as the grounds are beautiful. After the farm tour, Farmer Maria brings out a lovely selection of homemade cakes and flapjack, coffee and tea which you can enjoy while the kids play in the field which is full of old tractors and hay bales. Cost is £7 per person which includes a tractor ride at the end of the day.'
Nickkie, mum to Katie and Alice

Museums

Beaulieu
Beaulieu, Brockenhurst, Hampshire, SO42 7ZN
01590 612345
www.beaulieu.co.uk

'We visited in August 2012 on the bank holiday weekend and had a fantastic time – there is so much to do here you can easily spend all day and still have things left to do! It was busy when we visited as there was a classic car show event on which my car-obsessed husband and son loved! I would recommend that you book tickets in advance to avoid the queues when you arrive. Our favourite part was the Bond car section which was just amazing to see them in all their glory and you can get up close and personal to all the cars and bikes. We also loved the Top Gear section which was hilarious to see all the modified vehicles. My son particularly liked the big classic cars and the old bikes and was amazed by the falconry display which took place in the beautiful Abbey grounds – it was easily the best display we have seen as the birds flew right over our heads!
The grounds are beautiful for walks and picnics although we chose to eat in their restaurant. We were pleasantly surprised at all the choices for children – there were many options including healthy options for children and you could also buy a picnic style bag with five items for under £5 (including fruit). We opted for chicken nuggets and chips for our son which he loved and we also got free colouring crayons and paper – great! The baby changing rooms were great and they had plenty of highchairs available. We also spotted a microwave where you could heat up your

own food and also free water – they have really thought of things to help families out, which is fantastic. There was so much to do here – I'm sure we didn't get to do everything!'
Victoria, mum to Freddy

Brooklands Museum

Brooklands Road, Weybridge, KT13 0QN
01932 857381
www.brooklandsmuseum.com

'Racing cars, motorcycles, military and civilian aircraft and even buses, *Brooklands Museum* has it all for the budding transport enthusiast. From sitting in a Formula One car, to a passenger jet, an old World War Two bomber and even a fighter plane, Daniel had a great time pretending to fly or drive them all. There is a café with a small play area if parents or little ones need food or drinks.'
Stephen, dad to Daniel

The Look Out Discovery Centre

Nine Mile Ride, Bracknell, Berkshire, RG12 7QW
01344 354400
www.bracknell-forest.gov.uk/thelookoutdiscoverycentre

'A hands-on science museum for children in a lovely woodland setting with a café, lots of walks, bike trails and playgrounds outside. The exhibits enthral the children – my son can spend ages in the water zone playing with the boats in the canal system … with aprons and driers on hand nearby! There are also a variety of shows at the weekends and school holidays such as Yucky You, space and dinosaurs. There are special toddler days throughout the year for younger visitors.'
Leigh, mum to Ries and Elsa

'This is a hands-on science centre with lots of fun things to play with. It is set within Bracknell Forest, which is great for walking and cycling. There is also a lovely play area near the *Look Out Centre*.'
Louise, mum to Joe, Emilia and Sam

Milestones Museum

Leisure Park, Churchill Way West, Basingstoke, Hampshire, RG22 6PG
01256 477766
www3.hants.gov.uk/milestones/family-visits.htm

'*Milestones Museum* in Basingstoke is a living museum. They have a real life sweet

shop where you can spend an old fashioned penny for a quarter of sweets, and for the mums and dads an old fashioned fully operating pub! Our highlight was the Post Office where your little one can go in, dress up like a postman and sort letters and parcels etc. They quite often have special events on such as a Lego event that we attended.'
Joanne, mum to George

Science Museum
Exhibition Road, London, SW7 2DD
020 7942 4000
www.sciencemuseum.org.uk

'The best bit about the *Science Museum* is the Launchpad area. This is a hands-on area where the children get to try lots of experiments. It is probably designed for school-age children, but my youngest loves it too.'
Louise, mum to Joe, Emilia and Sam

Steam Trains
Also see the *Things to Do* chapter for other steam train activities.

Watercress Line
Station Road, Alton, Hampshire, GU34 2PZ (other stations are Alresford, Ropley and Medstead)
01962 733810
www.watercressline.co.uk

'We had a great day out here. The steam train runs through some lovely countryside from Alton to Alresford with a couple of stops along the way. It took us about 25 minutes to drive there from Guildford, then the train journey to Alresford was around 40 minutes. We decided to leave the buggy at home which I was pleased about as there are a lot of steps at Alton station, although we did see other families with buggies. If it's sunny, then take a picnic as there are lots of picnic tables at the stations. We went on a cold day in March so we had lunch at the *Pizza Express* in Alresford which caters very well for little ones. The *Watercress Line* also runs special events throughout the year so it's worth checking the website.'
Gemma, mum to Daniel

'Matthew is mad about Thomas so when we saw A Day out with Thomas on the *Watercress Line* we had to go. Matthew's grandparents came with us. The weather was not great but everyone there seemed to be having a good time. You could have a ride on Toad who was being pulled by Thomas. You could also have a ride

on Diesel. There were queues but the wait was worth it. You could ride the length of the railway on the normal steam train, and get on and off at the stations along the way. They had a craft area inside one station with face painting for the older children, and a bouncy castle at another. If your children like Thomas then this is definitely worth going to.'
Debbie, mum to Matthew

Theme Parks

Merlin Pass
www.merlinannualpass.co.uk

'A *Merlin Pass* gives you free access to Legoland, *Chessington World of Adventures* and various other places including Sea Life Centres. Although the passes are quite expensive, you don't have to use them many times before you've covered your costs. The one thing to bear in mind is that you still have to pay parking costs on each visit unless you have a premium pass.
The theme parks all do a parent pass, which you can pick up from customer services on arrival. The pass means one parent (and any older children) can queue for the bigger rides, while the other parent looks after younger children. At the end of the ride, the parents can swap, and the one who hasn't queued can get straight on without queuing.'
Louise, mum to Joe, Emilia and Sam

'On paper the *Merlin Pass* is not cheap, but it pays for itself in three to four visits, so well worth it if you have children that love theme parks! Places you get entry to locally are *Chessington* and Legoland (both within a 45 minute drive), also Thorpe Park, but that's not so good with young children. If you head up to London you can also get into the London Eye and Sea Life (especially good value if you can visit several times, as you wouldn't want to spend hours there with a toddler on a single day ticket, but if you're able to, it's a wonderful place to pop into for an hour at a time), both near Waterloo, and Madam Tussaud's a bit further afield. Young children go free to most attractions, so you won't need to get a pass for under-threes, but much less than that and they'll probably struggle with a whole day at a theme park, so best for slightly older children and/or babies who can chill in the pram.'
Katie, mum to Sebastian and Alexander

Chessington World of Adventures

Leatherhead Road, Chessington, KT9 2NE
0871 663 4477
www.chessington.com

'*Chessington* offers a toddler and adult special ticket for £15 during the week. I went with a group of my NCT friends, our small babies and toddlers and we had a great day. All rides were open in the park and the facilities for children were brilliant – bottle warmers, microwaves, baby chairs and comfortable baby changing facilities made the visit easier and fun. We took a picnic and there was lots of green space for the children to run around in. When you arrive the best thing to do is to go to the Adventurers' Services where you can pick up your child safety wristband and your Parent Swap ticket – this allows parents to still enjoy the height-restricted rides when visiting with toddlers, and you only have to queue once. After swapping over, the second rider gains entry via the ride exit – a handy thing to know! There are lots of rides suitable for toddlers and I would recommend this as a real treat in the summer. You can easily fill a day and have happy, exhausted and sleepy children at the end of it! Be aware that the toddler and adult ticket can only be booked online and is not available in August due to school summer holidays!!'
Rebecca, mum to Isobel and George

'We went as a group of six mums when our babies were around nine months old and had a fun day out. We bought Adult and Toddler tickets (currently £15) which have to be booked in advance as they are only available online for certain days but they worked out as the cheapest option. There is plenty for babies and toddlers to see including a zoo and a Sea Life Centre. We also took the little ones on a few of the tamer rides such as the Bubbleworks Water Ride and Tiny Truckers. We went on a weekday in April when it was really quiet so we didn't have to queue. There are lots of options for lunch – we went to Pizza Pasta and managed to get six highchairs and they didn't seem to mind us bringing our own baby food. The park is baby-friendly with buggy parks outside some of the rides and baby changing.'
Gemma, mum to Daniel

Paultons Park

Ower, Romsey, Hampshire, SO51 6AL
023 8081 4442
www.paultonspark.co.uk

'My nieces and nephew have been to *Paultons Park* and loved it. They wanted to go again and invited us to go along. Matthew was 14 months when we went in October half term. The park was not too busy, although there were long queues for

the rides in Peppa Pig World. There were quite a few rides that Matthew could go on which was good. *Chessington World of Adventures* has more to keep the little ones entertained because of the animals as well as the theme park rides. However, we did enjoy our day out at *Paultons Park*. My nieces and nephew even got me to go on some of the bigger rides. They had a great time whilst I was waiting for the ride to end!'
Debbie, mum to Matthew and auntie to Megan, Jessie and Daniel

'I have been to *Paultons Park* lots of times and every time it's been really fun! There are lots of rides for the little ones but also more adventurous ones for parents and older siblings. I recommend that you stay all day there because there are plenty of places to eat or you can buy food from the restaurant. Peppa Pig World does get a bit busy as it is still quite new, but the queues are worth it for the younger members of the family! Everyone that went with me thought that it was a very enjoyable day for all of the family.'
Megan, cousin to Matthew

'Peppa Pig World is a fantastic day trip to take kids from around two years to five years. A bit of a trek down the M3, *Paultons Park* is located near Southampton, but I would thoroughly recommend it as a special day out. The park is kept clean, has plenty of loos and changing facilities. There are a number of places to either buy lunch or take a picnic. A lot of it is under canopy, brilliant for sunny or rainy days.
The rides are well thought out and perfect for this younger age group. The constant excitement of running between Granpa Pig's Train and Miss Rabbit's Helicopter Ride will tire out both you and your toddler!
If you have time there is also a huge soft play area, outdoor park and splash park with a muddy puddle theme.
Watch out for the ice creams – over £7 for three – and the souvenir shop which is fairly pricey too. Other than that it's brilliant and worth a visit. Queues can be quite long during peak season, but no more than you would expect at any other theme park.'
Shelley, mum to Harriet and Hugo

Special Events

There are seasonal activities to do throughout the year at a variety of venues including visits from Father Christmas at theme parks and children's farms, fireworks on Bonfire Night in *Stoke Park*, the annual raft race at *Millmead*, the Guildford Book Festival and Peppa Pig Week at the *Watercress Line* to name but a few. It is well worth checking out the websites of your favourite locations to see when to go to make your visit extra special.

Surrey County Show

Stoke Park, London Road, GU1 1TU
01483 890810
www.surreycountyshow.co.uk

'The *Surrey County Show* is one of our favourite days of the year! My family and I have been going for years and it is always a fantastic day out. There are a mixture of local food and craft tents, rare British breeds, show jumping and livestock shows and various demonstrations (including cooking, dog shows and motorbike displays). Beatrice loves looking at all the animals (many of which can be petted) as well as the bouncy castles and various children's activities available. It is very family and dog friendly!

Parents are offered a wristband for their children to wear at the show, on which they can write their telephone numbers, in case the child goes missing.

Baby changing facilities are located on the showground near the Nightingale Road entrance, and loos are located throughout the showground. Parking at the showground is free, available on the north side of *Stoke Park*.'

Alex, mum to Beatrice and Magnus

'The *Surrey County Show* takes place in *Stoke Park* on the late May bank holiday weekend, and is a great day out for families. There is loads of parking on-site and we went with our little baby when he was just a few weeks old, and he absolutely loved it (we believe!). We took him in the sling as the pram would have been a bit harder to manage, but actually there were plenty of people there with prams. In 2012 it cost £12 for adults, £5 for children (tickets bought in advance) and under-fives went free. As well as the livestock shows, there were lots of animals to look at and pet, music, dog displays, a motorbike stunt team, farm machinery (great for sitting in for young kids!) and birds of prey. But our favourite place of all is always the food hall, which has a great range of food and drink in the form of a farmers' market. My only difficulty was that the baby change facilities weren't great (a small corner table-top in the disabled toilets) and there was nowhere to feed baby – as it was raining we had to go back to the car – but this won't stop us going again. A great day out for all ages.'

Suzie, mum to Alexander

Switching on the Christmas Lights

'Guildford town centre is buzzing with excitement! We saw carol singers at Westfield and on the High Street. Had an early dinner and then watched the lights switch on. Quite magical.'

Tara, mum to Elliott

3. Houses and Gardens
Tracy Liennard, mum to Eliza and Wilfred

There are a wealth of houses and gardens to visit in the area. Do consider visiting those that are not *National Trust* as well as those that are.

The review below succinctly highlights all the benefits of visiting *National Trust* properties – from beautiful gardens and grounds to wear out your energetic toddler to fabulous houses to stroll around, not forgetting cafés in which to have yummy treats. Membership is well worthwhile if you want to make these places a part of your regular routine.

National Trust Venues
www.nationaltrust.org.uk

'We've recently joined the *National Trust* and I had always thought these were places for grown-ups, however, I have been pleasantly surprised to find that they are just as enjoyable for families. Many venues have quizzes for the children to do whilst walking around with the grown-ups. Some houses have slings or hip carrying belts for baby, so parents/grandparents can walk around without fear of baby damaging any of the priceless pieces on display and baby is secure. The grounds surrounding many of these houses are ideal places to let the children safely run free or have a picnic. With our grandson we have visited *Polesden Lacey* and *Hatchlands Park* near Guildford, and Mottisfont in Romsey, Hampshire. All have been excellent with good clean baby changing facilities. There are many more places in and around the Guildford area. *Hatchlands Park* has a lake with ducks and cows in the field, both of which our grandson found fascinating. Many have events during the year such as Easter Egg hunts. Cafés are of a good clean standard with highchairs, and I believe most larger *National Trust* places do children's menus.

Membership is well worth taking out, you can visit and revisit as many venues as often as you like, for whatever length of time you like, without the pressure of

spending yet more money. Under-fives go free.
Have a look at the website, I think you will be impressed.'
Maggie, nana to Ellis

Also see *Devil's Punch Bowl* and *River Wey and Godalming Navigations and Dapdune Wharf* in the *Parks, Walks and Woodlands Chapter*.

Clandon Park
West Clandon, GU4 7RQ
01483 222482
www.nationaltrust.org.uk/clandon-park

'This is a *National Trust* property with lovely gardens to walk around, and a quiz available for older children. In the summer you can sometimes borrow equipment for lawn games which are great fun. After a visit here we usually wander further down the road to *Clandon Park Garden Centre* (also see page 58) which has a good coffee shop. There is also a pet shop by the garden centre, which has lots of reptiles. The children love going here and are fascinated by the snakes, lizards, bearded dragons and gecko.'
Louise, mum to Joe, Emilia and Sam

'The ultimate in virtually free entertainment – provided you are a *National Trust* member. Park in the *National Trust* car park and explore the gardens of this gorgeous Palladian mansion. There's a secret sunken garden, a huge sequoia tree and an intriguing Maori meeting house shipped over from New Zealand in the 19th century. If you are brave and your children are well behaved there is a lovely café and some fabulous art in the house. If you aren't (or they are not!) head along the drive to the garden centre (also see page 58), where there is a kid-friendly café and a chance to let off steam outside among the plant stock. When you think you are about to be booted out, head across the car park to the pet centre to check out bearded dragons, huge snakes, tropical fish and turtles and occasionally baby chameleons, which are officially the cutest things in the world. Don't let the children rap on the glass of the vivariums though or you will be told off. And don't look into the counter at the front of the shop if you don't like jumpy things.'
Katie, mum to Beth and Asa

Claremont Landscape Garden
Portsmouth Road, Esher, KT10 9JG
01372 467806
www.nationaltrust.org.uk/claremont-landscape-garden

'A *National Trust* property near Esher which makes a lovely walk and has easy paths

for pushchairs with a large lake to walk around. There are ducks to feed, hills to roll down and a little thatched cottage with some traditional games to explore. If little legs need some encouragement there is a good playground and lovely café at the end. The only downside is that the toilets are out in the car park so a travel potty is useful if your children are at that age.'
Leigh, mum to Ries and Elsa

'This is a *National Trust* garden near Esher. It has a lake to walk around, and you can buy food to feed the ducks and black swans. There is a wooden playground, and a big hill that is fun to climb. There is a café at the gardens or alternatively we sometimes head to *Garsons* Farm (also see page 19) which is a garden centre nearby (on Winterdown Road, off West End Lane). There is a good café here, and another play area. The farm shop and pick-your-own are also very good.'
Louise, mum to Joe, Emilia and Sam

'This is a really peaceful place to wander around with a huge lake and a grass amphitheatre to walk up. There are signs and a frequently updated map of what there is to see and it feels as though you're always discovering new areas. It's great for older children as there's a playground and also skittles and hobby horses to be found. It is really buggy-friendly and the café serves lovely hot and cold food and of course, great cake.'
Claire, mum to Orson

Hatchlands Park
East Clandon, GU4 7RT
01483 222482
www.nationaltrust.org.uk/hatchlands-park

'We've never been in the house but the grounds are fantastic. There are beautiful bluebell woods, plenty of space for picnics and fenced off ponds with plenty of wildlife to spot. It can be done with buggies although the more off-road they are, the easier it will be. We've been several times and rarely see anyone else as it's so big. The café serves hot and cold food and there are baby changing facilities in the toilets.'
Claire, mum to Orson

'A lovely *National Trust* property near East Clandon with beautiful grounds for the children to run around in. Wizard Wix's Willow Warren – a new natural playground in a copse of trees – has made it even easier to convince them to go for a walk and their 'fun days' include games on the lawn, arts and crafts, pony rides and there are family trails both in the garden and house for different age groups.'
Leigh, mum to Ries and Elsa

HOUSES AND GARDENS

Polesden Lacey
Great Bookham, Near Dorking, RH5 6BD
01372 452048
www.nationaltrust.org.uk/polesden-lacey

'*Polesden Lacey* has a big *National Trust* car park and really interesting grounds to explore. There's a house we've never visited but the grounds are spacious for picnicking, playing and walking around. There's an adventure playground, they keep bees and chickens and there are lovely tended gardens to walk through. You can do it with a buggy although the more off-road it is, the easier you'll find it.'
Claire, mum to Orson

Winkworth Arboretum
Hascombe Road, Godalming, GU8 4AD
01483 208477
www.nationaltrust.org.uk/winkworth-arboretum

'Totally buggy-unfriendly, but pop tinies into slings and let bigger ones run themselves ragged on the glorious rhododendron-covered slopes. Breathtaking displays when the trees take on their autumn colours. No bells and whistles, just a gorgeous lakeside setting for outdoor adventures. The café is sometimes open for restorative hot chocolate and cake.'
Katie, mum to Beth and Asa

'Open all year round, we love visiting the arboretum any time of year. They've got a number of different coloured routes clearly marked, suitable for all, whether heavily pregnant, pushing buggies or trying to tire out exuberant children. There's free parking, a café and baby change facilities, and you'll be given a map on entry. As with *National Trust* properties in general, they keep displays interesting and varied, so there's always something new to see.'
Suzie, mum to Alexander

Other Houses and Gardens

Hampton Court Palace
East Molesey, KT8 9AU
0844 482 7777
www.hrp.org.uk/HamptonCourtPalace

'There are free gardens to walk around, or you can pay to go into the palace gardens. There is a café and a gift shop. You can also get lost in the *Hampton Court* maze,

which is great fun. The Palace is alongside the river, which is a nice place for a stroll or a boat trip.'
Louise, mum to Joe, Emilia and Sam

Kew Gardens
Kew, Richmond, TW9 3AB
020 8332 5655
www.kew.org

'My toddler loved our recent visit to *Kew Gardens*, not only are there acres of green space to run around, there is a lovely section devoted to kids. There is a large outdoor playground including a zip wire for older children and also an imaginatively designed indoor playground in case it rains. My daughter played here for well over two hours without getting bored. There is also a café (one of several in *Kew Gardens*) just next door catering for children and adults alike. Alternatively you can bring your own food and have a picnic. We also explored the tree top walkway, which is perfectly safe for toddlers. There are shops to buy a whole range of items including books and toys for children. The car park is a hefty £6.50 but this is for all day, and you can easily enjoy a good five to six hours here. A wonderful alternative to *Wisley* (see page 34) and well worth a day out.'
Tracy, mum to Eliza and Wilfred

Loseley Park
Stakescorner Road, GU3 1HS
01483 304440
www.loseleypark.co.uk

'*Loseley Park* has a variety of events including craft fairs, agricultural shows and musical events. The house is beautiful and the walled gardens are stunning. There is a small café which can get very busy and there is also a shop. It is a good afternoon outing to take toddlers.'
Alex, mum to Beatrice and Magnus

The Medicine Garden
Downside Road, Cobham, KT11 3LU
01932 589536
www.themedicinegarden.com

'This is a lovely walled garden with a toddler play area, sandpit and baby change. There are big indoor and outdoor cafés and a little shop where you can buy birthday cards and other bits and bobs. The cake is excellent and the decking area is really pretty with sunshades.'
Catherine, mum to Leon

'Gorgeous walled Victorian garden – en route to Cobham, near Downside. We often enjoy whiling away an hour or two with friends in the serenity of the beautiful garden. A recently expanded children's play area with large sandpit keeps the little ones busy, whilst the mummies can enjoy lunch or a yummy cake from the Hothouse café. Plenty of space to sit outside. Regular weekly events for the grown-ups include Bootcamp, Yoga and Tai Chi. There is a fantastic garden shop, and some expensive but lovely gift shops, along with a treatment room if you feel like spoiling yourself. *The Medicine Garden* also has a great programme of seasonal family friendly events, including summer, Halloween and Christmas parties, Christmas market and summer concerts and theatre. Well worth a visit!'
Ruth, mum to George and William

RHS Garden Wisley
Woking, GU23 6QB
0845 260 9000
www.rhs.org.uk/Gardens/Wisley
(Also see *RHS Garden Wisley* on page 138)

'*Wisley* is ten minutes along the A3 from Guildford and costs £11 to get in. However, membership is £38 at the moment and you can take a guest for free every time. There are a couple of cafés that serve hot and cold food and there are toilets and baby change facilities. It is a brilliant place to take children as they can run around and make lots of noise while surrounded by beautiful plants, trees and flowers. There are ponds with ducks and fishes, an adventure playground made of natural materials and a hide where you can look out for birds and other wildlife using pictures on the walls.'
Claire, mum to Orson

'I joined *RHS Wisley* when they had a special offer which meant it was cheaper for me to join for the year than pay for me, my daughter and my parents. I'm so glad I did as we probably go there every couple of weeks now (especially when the weather is nice). The gardens are absolutely beautiful and so peaceful. There is so much room for the kids to run off steam safely and lots of interesting 'hide and seek' areas in which to play. The café is excellent with lovely children's lunch boxes and I am always made to feel very welcome by the staff who often help me juggle buggy and tray of food!'
Sarah, mum to Alice

'*RHS Wisley* membership was one of the best new baby presents I got: *Wisley* is beautiful all year and is a great option for those days with a new baby when you desperately need to get out of the house. It is breastfeeding friendly and has a

number of cafés to grab coffee with NCT buddies. It is also perfect for small children to explore as it is so varied but on a manageable scale. Baby changing is often oversubscribed and could do with an expansion.'
Amy, mum to Thomas and Oliver

'A perfect place to take children, with something for everyone. There are the beautiful gardens to walk/run around, ducks and fish to feed, a huge glasshouse to explore, a large play area and a small soft play area inside the restaurant for younger children.'
Louise, mum to Joe, Emilia and Sam

'A great place to meet up with friends. Always something new to see with the changing of the seasons, and routes that are buggy-friendly. A mouthwatering selection of food in the various cafés and good baby changing facilities. The annual membership is well worth it for maternity leave and beyond.'
Carla, mum to Ellis

'Get yourself a single membership here – it covers two adults, and babies/toddlers go free. A great place to go for walks with babies in prams but also for toddlers as they can roam free in relative safety. There are also play areas for older children. The duck pond is a favourite destination, followed by lunch in one of the cafés. There are plenty of highchairs and the Conservatory Café also has a small soft play area for those wet days. During the holidays it is much busier but there are plenty of organised events for children. The Butterfly event in February is always a big hit with the toddlers.'
Vicky, mum to Amelia

'Situated just off the A3, you can't find a better or indeed more beautiful place to take a stroll with your little one than *Wisley Gardens*. Not only is it a little corner of paradise but its size and varied layout makes it a must for all!
Parking is aplenty and the membership option is well worth it if you plan to make more than two trips in a year (we've already done six in just a few months!). There is just so much to explore that we still have a huge amount to get through! You have the option of flat or hilly walking, play and picnic areas, the glasshouse, lake and ponds to name but a few.
The cafés are very nice and there are several of them. Although on the expensive side, the food is of the homemade variety and I would recommend the hot chocolate. It is to die for and has fast become my favourite treat!! A must for any exhausted mummy! The gift shop is also fantastic and has something for everyone. I just know that *Wisley* is a place that we will be visiting for many years to come and that my son is going to continue to enjoy it, as he and *Wisley* grow together.'
Abi, mum to Oliver

HOUSES AND GARDENS

The Savill Garden
Wick Lane, Englefield Green, TW20 0UU
Parking off Wick Road, TW20 0XD for sat navs
01784 435544
www.theroyallandscape.co.uk/landscape/savillgarden

'*The Savill Garden* (adult entry £8.50) is a beautiful ornamental garden next to *Virginia Water Lake* (see pages 46 and 111) which also has a lovely gift shop and large sit down restaurant. There are baby change facilities and for those with toddlers and older children, a new children's play area is a short walk away close to the Obelisk Lawn. Open all year round, it is a beautiful place to take a stroll around, get some fresh air and tire out the little ones!'
Kathryn, mum to Amelie

Stoke Park Gardens
Stoke Road, GU1 1EP
(Also see *Stoke Park* on pages 39,48 and 111)

'Since our little one was born, we've been regular visitors to *Stoke Park* and in particular the Gardens at the bottom end (near the Lido). In the early days it was a great place to get out of the house for a bit of fresh air and greenery (and often a bit of peace and quiet as our daughter would often go to sleep too – a definite bonus!). I've enjoyed watching the trees and flowers through the seasons, and my NCT group has even managed a few picnics in the odd bits of sunshine we've had this year. I think we'll continue to enjoy the gardens in future as our little one gets older – there's what looks like a great playground, and in the summer a paddling pool and mini golf. There's also a little kiosk for ice cream and drinks, toilets and tennis courts. All in all a good place to get out and enjoy the outdoors right on our doorstep.'
Bronwen, mum to Olwen

4. Parks, Walks and Woodlands
Tracy Liennard, mum to Eliza and Wilfred

Spring, summer, autumn, winter and spring again. Whatever the season, the parks, walks and woodlands around Guildford are a perfect opportunity to get off the pavements and immerse yourself in nature. Guildford is splat bang in the middle of the North Downs and lots of fantastic countryside.

If you take the opportunity to venture away from the high street and out into the countryside that surrounds Guildford, you will find many hours of walks to enjoy and explore with your child, providing a great place for them to run riot (or sleep peacefully in their buggy or carrier) and just admire the views that many other parents in England aren't lucky enough to live near.

Parks

Broadwater Park
Summer's Road, Godalming, GU7 3BH

'A quick walk around the pond (about 15 minutes in one go – more with a toddler!) with lots of ducks to see and feed. If you are lucky (and quiet) you might see the fishermen catch something. A nice easy path for buggies and you can extend your walk around the cricket field at the top end if you'd like to go five minutes further. There is also a great playground and The Manor Inn opposite can provide refreshments if needed.'
Carla, mum to Ellis

'*Broadwater Park* is a fabulous playground for the kids. We visited on a Saturday afternoon and it was busy but not unpleasantly so. There is a lot of equipment and a lot of variety including the usual jungle gym, swings and slides but also a sandpit and a zip line. There is a section for tots and also an area for older children.

Next door is a basketball court and it is situated in a park near the cricket club and Godalming Leisure Centre which has parking. It is worth driving to for a change from your usual swings and slides.

If you follow the path to the right just past the toilets there is a lake which you can walk around and feed the ducks and fish. The girls were particularly excited by the huge fish eating the bread for the ducks. As Lia said, "they are bigger than you can imagine". A lovely afternoon.'

Tracy, mum to Eliza and Wilfred and aunt to Lia and Yasmin

Brooklands Community Park
Sopwith Drive, Weybridge, KT13 0YU
www.elmbridge.gov.uk/leisure/parks/brooklands.htm

'A fabulous place to learn to scoot or ride bikes. There are lots of tarmac tracks all visible from everywhere so you can watch easily as children get more independent. There is also a playground for when they want a break from pedalling.'

Leigh, mum to Ries and Elsa

Bushy Park
Hampton, TW11 0EQ
www.royalparks.org.uk/parks/bushy-park

'*Bushy Park* is a wonderful park just opposite *Hampton Court Palace* (see page 32). It has a large enclosed playground with lots of separate climbing frames etc. and a large sandpit. There is a lake to walk around, with deer roaming freely around the park. Further into the park there is the Pheasantry Café, which has its own car park, and is set within enclosed wooded gardens (with no deer). The park is a lovely place for children to explore. Afterwards, you can head to *Hampton Court Palace*.'

Louise, mum to Joe, Emilia and Sam

Farnham Park
Farnham, GU9 0AG

'*Farnham Park* is a hidden gem behind the castle in Farnham. It has two lovely playgrounds, one for older children which has a zip wire and lots of more challenging climbing frames and a newly refurbished playground which has lots for under-fives. It is also a beautiful park for picnics or just a gentle stroll. There is plenty of free parking up by the golf club or in surrounding streets. Makes a nice, quieter change from *Alice Holt* (see page 40).'

Joanne, mum to George

Goldsworth Park Lake
Wishbone Way, Woking

'Right in the middle of the Goldsworth Park estate in Woking, the lake is a lovely spot for a morning out. Park in Waitrose car park and head up the lane by the church and you get to the bottom end of the lake. The path goes all the way round, probably a good 30 minute walk at toddler speed, less with an older child or by yourself with a buggy (the path is concrete, buggy-friendly). Half way round is a great little play park with a couple of climbing frames, toddler swings, slides and even a zip wire. Feed the ducks (and, if you're lucky, swans) on the lake and perhaps finish by popping into Waitrose to take something yummy home for lunch.'
Katie, mum to Sebastian and Alexander

Priory Park
Bell Street, Reigate, RH2 7RL

'This is a great free trip out! Situated in the middle of Reigate Priory (off Bell Street in the heart of Reigate) is a wooden ship surrounded by sand, water squirters and traditional wooden play equipment. A lovely place to meet for all ages! While you're there you can even walk to the lake and feed the ducks, so don't forget your bread! A café is situated next to the park for your coffee, ice creams and even pizza! But if you fancy something more, Reigate High Street is in walking distance with plenty of shops and restaurants and so is Morrisons supermarket which does great value kids meals. Open all year, but best in the summer!'
Nickkie, mum to Katie and Alice

Queen Elizabeth Country Park
Gravel Hill, Horndean, Hampshire, PO8 0QE
www3.hants.gov.uk/qecp

'Situated a few miles from Portsmouth, this is just off the A3. There are varying routes depending on the distance you would like to cover. Off-road buggy-friendly as long as you don't mind a few steep hills. It's best to park at the top if you want to avoid them! Barbecues and shelters can be rented if you want to make a day of it with friends and family. Lots of lovely woodland to explore. Cafés and toilets with changing facilities are stationed at the two main bases.'
Carla, mum to Ellis

Stoke Park
Stoke Road, GU1 1EP
(Also see *Stoke Park* on pages 36, 48 and 111)

'*Stoke Park* is a brilliant place to spend lots of free time. There is a toilet block with a changing station where the only hot water tap is situated. There is a little café selling ice creams and drinks which has picnic tables outside. There is plenty of space for running around and picnicking or you can visit the playground, sensory garden, boating lake or paddling area. There's a lake with ducks and also tennis courts and crazy golf depending on how old your children are.'
Claire, mum to Orson

'*Stoke Park* is probably the biggest park in Guildford with lots to do including tennis courts, mini golf, large playground, duck pond and model boat pond, sensory garden, rose garden, snack kiosk, skate park and summer paddling pool, as well as a huge green area for sports. The playground is good fun with a separate area for younger toddlers, a large climbing frame and a tall helter-skelter slide. It is nearly always busy with children of all ages so avoid the after-school rush if you can! It's a great place to bring scooters and balance bikes as the smooth paths go for miles. The boat pond is pretty with a bridge leading over to an island in the middle where you will often find ducks and little ducklings in the spring. The sensory garden has been specially planted to appeal to children through fragrance and touchability. The paddling pool is a fantastic free facility on hot summer days (open from Easter to end August approx) where youngsters can cool off by splashing about in the shallow water, and there is lots of shade around near the pool for picnics. Free two-hour parking in the College car park/along Nightingale Road but check the signs.'
Jenny, mum to Abigail and Alistair

Wellington Country Park
Odiham Road, Riseley, Near Reading, RG7 1SP
www.wellington-country-park.co.uk

'This is a bit of a trek from Guildford, but definitely worth the journey if you have a few hours to spend. It has lots to offer for children of all ages, but probably more suited to those that are already mobile and adventurous. There are several playground areas, a sand pit, bouncing pillow, crazy golf, an animal farm and a train. Train rides are not included in the entry fee and are £1 extra, although under-twos are free.'
Debbie, mum to Matthew

Walks and Woodlands

Alice Holt Forest
Bucks Horn Oak, Farnham, GU10 4LS
01420 23666
www.forestry.gov.uk/aliceholt

'A forest with lots to do (and what is more, it makes for a cheap day out ... only parking charges to pay!). There are lots of different trails to walk including a family trail with massive sculptures that are actually play frames for the children. There are also several lovely playgrounds around the site, plenty of space to picnic, play games and scoot around. There is a café, baby changing facilities and if you are feeling a bit more energetic you can hire bikes or do *Pushy Mother* workouts (see page 92) ... although I can't vouch for these as I'm not that energetic!'
Leigh, mum to Ries and Elsa

'Routes of various lengths on varying terrain means there is something suitable for everyone. Lots of beautiful flowers and the odd animal to look out for on your way around. For older children the play area is huge and looks great fun. Small café and changing pod open all year.'
Carla, mum to Ellis

'*Alice Holt* is great. It's a really lovely wood with pram-friendly walks. You pay to park but it's free to get in so definitely worth a visit.'
Cat, mum to Poppy

'*Alice Holt* is brilliant alone or with a group, and for all ages. There are several walks around the woods, mostly buggy-friendly, including one specifically designed for buggies and young children, with lots of places marked to spot things (info sheet and maps of the walks available by car park pay machines). There is a fabulous playground for younger children with a massive pirate ship and a wide selection of baby and toddler swings, an adventure playground for older children, and it is also home to Go Ape (over tens only, charges apply). There is a small café serving good hot and cold food and drinks (including kids' lunch boxes) and toilets, including baby changing.
It's also brilliant for parties; you can hire the education centre classrooms (approx £40 for two hours) and the café will cater party food at very reasonable rates. My NCT group held the babies' first birthday party there with all the older siblings too and had a fantastic time playing in the playgrounds and stuffing ourselves with lovely food.'
Katie, mum to Sebastian and Alexander

Britten's Pond
Salt Box Road, Jacobs Well

'This is a lovely spot and the walk around the pond is short enough for little legs to manage. The pond is a popular place for fishing and my son loves seeing all the ducks, geese and other wildlife. The railway line runs next to it so there is the added

excitement of seeing a few trains too. It's best to take wellies for the little ones as it can be muddy in places. There are no facilities but the parking is free.'
Gemma, mum to Daniel

Devil's Punch Bowl
London Road, Hindhead, GU26 6AB
www.nationaltrust.org.uk/hindhead-and-devils-punchbowl

'*Devil's Punch Bowl* has a big *National Trust* car park with a café serving hot and cold food. They have baby change facilities in the toilets and there are buggy-friendly walks as well as muddier off-road walks. This is where the new Hindhead tunnel has been built and there are viewing platforms so it's a good place to take children to see how the cars disappear underground and let nature return to the area.'
Claire, mum to Orson

Fleet Pond
Fleet, Hampshire, GU51 3QY

'A nice walk around the pond with lots of wildfowl to see. It's actually the largest freshwater lake in Hampshire and a Site of Special Scientific Interest. The path is ok for buggies – although smaller wheels might get a bit stuck on tree roots. It's a bit tricky to find from the address, but there are brown signs from J4a of the M3. Very little in the way of facilities, but a good walk.'
Carla, mum to Ellis

Frensham Great Pond
Bacon Lane, Churt
www.waverley.gov.uk/info/200029/countryside/693/frensham_great_pond

'This is the next best thing to going to the seaside! There is a lovely sandy beach here and when we went the water was clean enough for a paddle (check on the website before you go). There is also a snack bar, picnic tables and toilets. Well worth the 40 minute drive from Guildford.'
Gemma, mum to Daniel

Millmead Lock
(behind *Debenhams* and the Yvonne Arnaud Theatre), GU1 3UU
(Also see *Millmead Lock* on pages 110 and 123)

'Duck feeding and picnics at *Millmead Lock* are a staple of the Guildford experience, not to mention the odd ice cream on warmer days. They are a guaranteed source of

free entertainment, and provide a welcome release from a trip to the shops. Access is easy, particularly early on Sunday mornings when the Millmead car park is currently free. Making the trip longer is simple with a gentle stroll along the relatively pushchair-friendly towpath a good option and offering a range of items of interest, including the lock, canal and rowing boats and cows grazing in Millmead meadow.'
Peter, dad to Thomas and Oliver

The Mount
GU2 4JD

'*The Mount* (Guildown) is a great climb which can be done with a buggy but is easier without if your baby likes being in a sling. It's a big steep hill which you can access from Farnham Road or Portsmouth Road and there are animals grazing if you keep walking along and through the little wood. It's great for kite flying and picnicking while looking out across what feels like the whole of Surrey. If you take the buggy, keep walking along the very top where the road becomes a track that takes you through the trees down to meet the A31 at the other end.'
Claire, mum to Orson

Newlands Corner
Shere Road, GU4 8SE
(Also see *Newlands Corner* on page 110)

'This is a good place to go to let your little one burn off some energy! My son always has lots of fun running up and down the hill then we like to sit and eat ice creams while enjoying the amazing views.'
Gemma, mum to Daniel

'There is a big car park and a serving hatch for tea and chocolate bars. We come here for great walking across open land with fantastic views, or through woods for a more adventurous walk. It's not very buggy-friendly so a sling or carrier is best and the toilets are pretty basic. It's a lovely place for a picnic and ball games in the sun or for a clamber through the woods if it's raining.'
Claire, mum to Orson

The Old Railway at Bramley
Station Road, Bramley

'Just off Station Road in Bramley is a little car park next to the old railway station. This disused line has been laid to path, with a good smooth concrete surface. You can take lovely walks in either direction but it comes into its own as a cycle track (you can cycle all the way to/from Guildford). Just along from the old station is a

little playground, and my son loves to bring his bike or scooter, take a trip up the path and back and stop off to play in the giant wooden train. Bramley village centre is also less than five minutes round the corner.'
Katie, mum to Sebastian and Alexander

The River Wey
(behind *Debenhams* and the Yvonne Arnaud Theatre), GU1 3UU

'*River Wey* walks tend to be better without a buggy although you can have a pleasant walk with one. If you follow the tow path from the White House pub and cross the little bridge at a good duck feeding spot (see *Millmead Lock* on pages 42,110 and 123) towards the Yvonne Arnaud Theatre, you soon get to the weir and canal boats. Keep going through the field areas with picnic tables and either head left towards the Boatman pub or go right and the tow path gets narrow and can be really muddy. After a while you can take a left before the bridge and come out on the Old Portsmouth Road and you can climb up to St Catherine's Church which is now a ruin but you can sit on the grass and feel the trains rumble underground. You can also search in the rabbit holes for old clay pipes from when it was a pilgrims' meeting and market place hundreds of years ago. Alternatively go right and walk back to town along the main road passing the Ship Inn which does great pizzas.'
Claire, mum to Orson

River Wey and Godalming Navigations and Dapdune Wharf
Wharf Road, GU1 4RR
01483 561389
www.nationaltrust.org.uk/river-wey-godalming-navigations-and-dapdune-wharf

'We really enjoy *Dapdune Wharf*. It's a lovely relaxed haven close to the centre of Guildford, with boats to climb on, a visitor centre and a boat trip to be taken into town. It's a *National Trust* property, so it helps if you have membership but it's one of the less expensive *National Trust* properties (currently £3.50 for an adult). There's plenty of free parking, a café with baby change facilities and it's an easy site for pushchairs.
The *River Wey Navigations* that link Guildford to Weybridge represent 15 miles of lovely terrain; most of it easily cycled or walked with a pram, with something like 20 pubs along the distance, so plenty of places for refreshment! The majority of the towpath is free to walk on and we have seen some lovely plants and wildlife on our many walks – the only thing is that we tend to avoid it on a wet day as the towpath near us gets very muddy, so maybe stick to *Dapdune Wharf* with a pram in the winter!'
Tony, dad to Alexander

Shere
GU5 9HE

'It is a nice place to spend a couple of hours to feed the ducks and walk around where the horses cross the ford. There are also a couple of cafés and a pub. They also have a playground (see page 50). It is an old town with a lot of history, so is a good place to take the kids when relatives visit.'
Tara, mum to Elliott

'The perfect place for Pooh Sticks: a crystal clear stream (the Tillingbourne), a picturesquely wonky bridge, a smattering of ducks and, once you are done, a tearoom to the left and a pub to the right.'
Katie, mum to Beth and Asa

South Bank
Waterloo, London

'It may be cheating to put a London location in a guide about Guildford and the

surrounding area, but sometimes you are itching to get out of Guildford and the *South Bank* is only a 35 minute train journey and a ten minute walk away. It is beautiful to walk along the river promenade and admire the iconic architecture. There is often something going on to engage your toddler (we last went during the Olympics and had a giant sand pit with rainbow coloured sand to play in on the river front). You can walk to the Tate Modern or visit a number of visitor attractions along the way, all without having to go near the Tube! It has long been my favourite part of London.'
Tracy, mum to Eliza and Wilfred

St Martha's Hill/Chantries Wood
Halfpenny Lane, Chilworth, GU4 8PY

'The hill is not one for buggies with all the sandy paths, but pop little ones in a sling and off you go. The woodlands are more manageable with a good buggy, but you can't go too far without going up or down a hill! Fantastic views and beautiful woodland (a trip during bluebell season is highly recommended – some of the best I have seen), as well as the church of St Martha-on-the-Hill at the top of the hill with lots of history (look it up before you go!). It is definitely worth the slog to get up there.
From St Martha's you have *Newlands Corner* (see pages 43 and 110) to one side and Pewley Down to the other with a network of footpaths linking them, including the North Downs Way and the beginning of the Downs Link. There are a number of car parks on *St Martha's Hill.*'
Carla, mum to Ellis

Virginia Water Lake
London Road, Virginia Water, GU25 4QF
www.theroyallandscape.co.uk/gardens-and-landscape/virginia-water
(Also see *Virginia Water Lake* on page 111)

'On the southern part of Windsor Great Park is *Virginia Water Lake*, close to Ascot. Apart from a fairly small car park charge (one hour £1.50, two hours £3) the lake and its beautiful woodland surroundings are free to walk around.
For those up for a bit of exercise, the buggy-friendly path around the lake is approximately 4.5 miles – roughly an hour and half walk. For the more adventurous, there are many other (less well trodden) paths to explore. There are a few coffee vans around the lake serving surprisingly good coffee, pastries, bacon sandwiches etc. and picnic tables dotted around for those in need of a rest or to feed.'
Kathryn, mum to Amelie

5. Playgrounds
Gemma Gregson, mum to Daniel

We are lucky to have lots of playgrounds in Guildford. Some are very small with just a few pieces of equipment and others are very big with lots of different swings, climbing frames and slides. Some are brilliant time fillers, perfect to pop into on the way home from the shops, while others merit a special trip out to them, perhaps combined with a walk or feeding the ducks. Whatever their type, they are all fantastic places to take toddlers to burn off some energy, interact with other children, and most of all, to have some fun.

We hope this chapter will help you discover a favourite playground or two, where you and your children can spend many an enjoyable hour together.

Central Guildford
(including Guildford Park, Onslow Village and the Town Centre)

Foxenden Quarry Playground
York Road, GU1 4DN
(Also see *Foxenden Quarry Playground* on page 122)

'Situated next to York Road car park, this playground has the usual equipment including a really long slide that my son enjoys although he does need a hand to get up there.'
Gemma, mum to Daniel

Onslow Recreation Ground
Wilderness Road, Onslow Village, GU2 7QP

'Onslow Village next to the Arboretum – a small playground which is great for stopping off after a walk through the Arboretum and there's a basketball hoop

and playing field for ball games too. There are toilets nearby but no baby change facilities.'
Claire, mum to Orson

The Oval Playground
The Oval, Guildford Park, GU2 7TP

'Corner of The Oval and The Chase – there's a small playing field next to a fenced off playground for older children and then a smaller playground fenced off within that for toddlers. It's rarely busy and is great for taking kids of mixed ages.'
Claire, mum to Orson

St Luke's Square Playground
Newlands Crescent, GU1 3JH

'Situated right next to St Luke's Surgery. This playground has two gated areas suitable for children up to around 10/11. There are three smaller slides in the infants' playground along with two ride-on toys. Exploratory infants will love the challenge of climbing the ladder in the 'big kids' area to go down the corkscrew slide. A perfect place to go for a quick play!'
Tara, mum to Elliot

Stoke Park Play Area
Stoke Road, GU1 1EP
(Also see *Stoke Park* on pages 36, 39 and 111)

'*Stoke Park* has a fantastic playground. It has lots of different slides including one large spiral one, swings, climbing frames, a seesaw and various animal shapes on springs to bounce on. If the weather is good, we like to combine a visit to the playground with a dip in the paddling pool which children of all ages seem to love. There is also a duck pond behind the paddling pool which is a popular spot for those with model boats and Daniel loves watching them race around the pond.'
Gemma, mum to Daniel

East Guildford
(including Burpham, Clandon, Gomshall, The Horsleys, Merrow, Send and Shere)

Bushy Hill Drive Playground
Bushy Hill Drive, Merrow, GU1 2UG

'*Bushy Hill Drive* play area is designed for toddlers and juniors. It is right next to the

community centre and a bus stop for the number 36 and 37 buses. It has a basketball court for teenagers and a large open green area to play in. The playground itself is divided into two areas, one for toddlers, the other for juniors. They both have the usual array of swings and slides. The toddlers' section has some musical chimes to play with and the older area has a nice jungle gym complete with a small climbing wall.'
Tracy, mum to Eliza and Wilfred

'Recently titivated, this little playground is often quiet when others are overrun. There's plenty of surrounding grass for scampering. Nothing amazing, but still with the potential to save your sanity when you are having one of those days.'
Katie, mum to Beth and Asa

Devoil Close Playground
Devoil Close, Burpham, GU4 7FQ

'We go to this playground most days. It is very small with one toddler swing, a seesaw type thing on a spring to bounce on and also a small climbing frame which includes a fireman's pole and a slide. Despite not having much equipment, Daniel loves it and as it is usually quiet it has been great for developing his physical abilities. We usually see the same faces in there so Daniel has made some friends too which is nice. It's probably not one that is worth driving to, but if you live within walking distance then it is definitely worth a visit.'
Gemma, mum to Daniel

Gomshall Playground
Goose Green, Gomshall, GU5 9LL (turn in just after the pub car park)

'*Gomshall Playground* is fantastic for children aged two years plus who will enjoy the large climbing frame, big slide, balance beams, stepping stones and best of all, the zip wire! My three-year-old has a particular passion for zip wires and this one is great as it's low enough to the ground that she can use it independently and has no fear of great injury if she falls off. There are also the usual swings and rockers. Most of this playground is made from wood and hence blends beautifully with its natural surroundings. There is also a large green for ball games/dog walking/picnics next to the playground. Gomshall's train station is not far, so you could incorporate a fun train journey to get there, and there is a very nice tea room called *Tillings Café* (see page 140) on the main road which serves children's meals.'
Jenny, mum to Abigail and Alistair

PLAYGROUNDS

Kingston Meadows Play Area
Kingston Avenue, East Horsley, KT24 6QT

'This playground is tucked down a side road and is next to East Horsley Village Hall. It has the usual type of equipment for children in two enclosed areas – swings, a seesaw and a pirate ship with a slide in one area, and the other has a roundabout, swings for older children and a large climbing frame with a slide. There is also an area for grown-ups and older children with gym-type equipment and a large structure for climbing. It's set in a lovely location surrounded by trees and there's also a football field, a BMX facility, tennis courts and a basketball hoop.'
Gemma, mum to Daniel

Send Recreation Ground
Send Road, Send, Woking, GU23 7EZ

'This is one of our favourite places to take our baby. As well as loads of play equipment for children (swings, roundabout and an enclosed area for little ones), the Rec has a table tennis table, tennis court, climbing wall, lots of seats, toilets, adult workout equipment and a ball court, and a huge grass area for picnics. In addition, the Rec is right next to a row of shops, meaning there is good parking and access to drinks and snacks as needed. Although our baby is too young to use the facilities himself, he really enjoys his daily walks through this well-loved park and can't wait to get going on the swings!'
Tony, dad to Alexander

Shere Recreation Ground
Upper Street, Shere, GU5 9HE
(Also see *Shere* on page 45)

'This enclosed playground is next to a large, free car park and behind Shere museum and Shere Village Hall. It's got some swings, a large slide, a small climbing frame, a couple of things to bounce on and some benches for parents to sit on. It's surrounded by lovely scenery and next to a large field.'
Gemma, mum to Daniel

Sutherland Memorial Park
Clay Lane, Burpham, GU4 7JU
(Also see *Sutherland Memorial Park* on page 111)

'A large enclosed playground split into two – one area for toddlers, the other for larger kids. Avoid 3.30pm at the end of the school day when the primary school

kids traipse out and take over for half an hour. An ice cream van is usually around on sunny days and weekends. My daughter loves going to this playground and I have met several local mums here who I also see at *Caterpillar Café* (see page 100).'
Vicky, mum to Amelia

West Clandon Playground
The Street, West Clandon, GU4 7TD

'A firm favourite with our two boys. Lovely, quiet playground with decent parking. For some reason it still seems quite undiscovered as we are often there by ourselves! A nice grassy spot with benches overlooking pretty views of the valley (for the grown-ups) and plenty of climbing frames, swings, zip wire etc – all the usual for the kids. We often combine a trip here with a visit to *Clandon Park Garden Centre* (see page 58) for cake and tea or kids' lunch.'
Ruth, mum to George and William

'This playground is next to West Clandon Village Hall, so there is plenty of parking. There is an enclosed toddler area with a climbing frame incorporating a tunnel and a slide. Next to this is a larger area probably aimed more at older children but my toddler enjoyed it too, with a roundabout, swings, a couple of large slides (one in particular was very good), springs to bounce on and a zip wire which was a hit with both my husband and son! We went one Saturday morning and it was very quiet but we had lots of fun. It's got a few picnic tables and it's surrounded by trees and fields so all very pleasant. A really good playground to go to if you are in the area.'
Gemma, mum to Daniel

West Horsley Playground
The Street, West Horsley, KT24 6DD

'This is a nice little playground. It's on the main road next to West Horsley Village Hall which has parking. The playground has some swings, a balance beam, rope bridges, a climbing frame with a slide, a roundabout and a basketball hoop. There is also a small structure in the shape of a train that my son really liked and this had a small slide on it too.'
Gemma, mum to Daniel

North Guildford
(including Bellfields, Jacobs Well and Stoughton)

Hazel Avenue Play Area
Hazel Avenue, Bellfields, GU1 1NS

PLAYGROUNDS

'The playground on Hazel Avenue is split into two play areas, linked by a gate. The one for smaller children has a good selection of equipment – baby swings, a slide/climbing frame with a cute picnic table underneath, see-saw, spinning bowl and some little seats. There's also a very small patch of grass to sit on. The area for older kids has swings, climbing frames and spinning discs to stand on. It's located next to a shop so handy for buying treats but does get busy with older children, often playing football, especially after school.'
Susan, mum to Thomas and Harry

Jacobs Well Play Area
White House Lane, Jacobs Well, GU4 7PT

'This is a lovely little local playground with a small grassy area for picnics and a large pond where you might even get to see baby geese! There are two baby swings, two swings for older children, a roundabout and a slide/climbing frame with tunnel. Cars being parked there are frowned upon by local residents (and you may get asked to move) so it's best to park round the corner in one of the residential streets or just walk. There's also a large grass area where kids often play football.'
Susan, mum to Thomas and Harry

Stoughton Recreation Ground
Worplesdon Road, Stoughton, GU2 9RT

'This is a large playground with several different areas for toddlers/young children and other enclosed areas for older children. This means that the younger ones can play without older children/teenagers getting in their way and vice versa. There is a whole range of equipment including a small trampoline and merry-go-round and the obvious swings, slides and jungle gym. There are also basketball hoops for older children. There is a large well-kept green space which the playground sits within, perfect for kids to run around, play on their bikes or have a picnic. Most of the equipment is for ages three and over, those who are younger will need help getting up onto the jungle gym. Worth a special visit if you have children of a variety of ages.'
Tracy, mum to Eliza and Wilfred

6. Things to Do

Tracy Liennard, mum to Eliza and Wilfred

As a result of helping to put this chapter together, I have had the opportunity to visit places I either didn't know existed or didn't realise how great they were. There are places to go for a quick half hour or places that can fill an entire morning or afternoon. Books (like *Tots About Town*), websites and friends' recommendations all help you to build up a range of places to explore and enjoy with your child. It is also well worth checking the free magazines for things that are happening in the coming months. Families Surrey West, Family Grapevine and ABC Magazine can be picked up in various places such as local libraries and *Children's Centres*.

Arts and Culture

G Live
London Road, GU1 2AA
0844 7701 797
www.glive.co.uk
(Also see *G Live* on page 133)

'*G Live* is a great new facility for Guildford and has brought some fantastic shows out of London and into the South East. I've already taken my daughter to see Peppa Pig and The Tiger who came to Tea. My husband is taking her to The Gruffalo later this year as the performance runs on a Saturday. The theatre is well laid out, with easy access for pushchairs and plenty of loos, if slightly aggressive hand dryers! But it's all very clean and well maintained. The tickets are all reasonably priced, but watch out for booking fees which can increase the cost significantly especially if booking online or over the phone.'
Shelley, mum to Harriet and Hugo

Odeon Newbies
Odeon, Bedford Road, GU1 4SJ
0871 224 4007
www.odeon.co.uk/fanatic/newbies

'Each week, the *Odeon* cinema does a special showing for you to bring babies along to. There is a different film every week. The house lights are kept up and the sound is somewhat quieter – the guy even comes down to check it's not too loud. During the course of a film, each baby takes their turn at 'being the noisy one' so you have no need to feel bad when it's your little bundle that's crying.'
Carla, mum to Ellis

'The Guildford *Odeon* runs film showings exclusively for parents/guardians and babies (*Odeon Newbies*). It's a great way to enjoy watching (well sort of!) a current film release and not having to worry about your little one making noise. You can feed them during the film or if they have a little doze through it even better ... you get to watch it properly!! The volume is slightly quieter and the lights a little more raised than usual providing a more comfortable environment. Film showings are usually weekday mornings, so you would need to check the listings in advance, and all films are 12A certificate or lower with ticket prices as normal and babies go for free. There is ample parking at the public car park near to the cinema.

I've taken my boy Charlie a few times now and have to say he's been totally fascinated by the big screen. There's no issue if you need to feed your baby, and if they get a little fractious you can always get up and walk them about at the back of the room. It's a fun thing to do on your own, with a friend or a group of friends, where you can still get your cinema fix even with your baby!'
Carolyn, mum to Charlie

Waterstones
71-73 High Street, GU1 3DY
0843 290 8357
www.waterstones.com
(Also see *Waterstones* on page 124)

'*Waterstones* regularly run free sessions for children during the school holidays, normally based around a story. The staff there are lovely and very enthusiastic. The sessions usually include a craft and we have come home with a potted sunflower and various collages in the past.'
Joanne, mum to George

Watts Gallery
Down Lane, Compton, GU3 1DQ
01483 810235
www.wattsgallery.org.uk

'A beautiful arts and crafts gallery exhibiting work by the Victorian painter and sculptor G F Watts as well as temporary exhibitions. There is a fantastic tea room (which serves gluten free food) and is child-friendly, and a lovely shop which is worth a visit. There is also a memorial chapel down the road designed by his wife Mary Watts which is well worth a visit.'
Alex, mum to Beatrice

Cars, Planes and Trains
(Also see *Beaulieu, Brooklands Museum* and the *Watercress Line* in *Days Out*)

Fairoaks Airport
Chobham, GU24 8HU
01276 857 700
www.fairoaksairport.com

'We were given *Fairoaks Airport* as a little place to go upon an afternoon as a

recommendation from a friend. We have since visited a couple of times and have not been disappointed. Yes – you cannot spend a whole day here but our little boy loved watching the aeroplanes take off and land so you can easily pass a couple of hours. This is a small airport so all the aeroplanes are small (I think light aircraft is the correct term!). They have a café which backs onto the runway and they even have little steps for children so they can get a better view of the planes! There are always plenty of families there enjoying the 'attraction' when we have been and of course this is free (except for anything you might spend in the café!). The café is open from 8.30am to 4pm and there are plenty of highchairs available. You can sit inside or outside. The food is as you would expect really but they do a nice selection of cakes!'
Victoria, mum to Freddy

Great Cockcrow Railway
Hardwick Lane, Lyne, Chertsey, KT16 0AD
01932 565474
www.cockcrow.co.uk

'This is a miniature railway near St. Peter's Hospital, Chertsey. It has two different routes you can travel. You can buy tickets for one or both routes. The children love sitting on the little trains. Under-twos are not allowed though. The railway is open every Sunday from May to October and also on a Wednesday in August.'
Louise, mum to Joe, Emilia and Sam

Guildford Model Engineering Society
Stoke Park, London Road, GU1 1TU
www.gmes.org.uk

'This is a brilliant place to spend a couple of hours. Situated at the far end of *Stoke Park* (by the Parkway/Boxgrove Road/London Road roundabout), the *Guildford Model Engineering Society* runs open afternoons on various Sundays in the year (March to October). Entrance is free, as is the parking. The main attraction is the steam train rides which seem to be a big hit with children and adults alike! They are very reasonably priced at 80p for one ride or £2 for three rides (under-threes go free) with a choice of two trains. They also have two large model railways which my two-year-old loved watching. There are a few sets of steps over the train tracks so if you take a buggy, be prepared to have to lift it up and down, although they do have a level crossing where you can ask staff for help over the tracks if needed. Refreshments are available and so are baby changing facilities. They also run a charity day once a year when they also have a bouncy castle. My son thought it was fab – train rides and a bouncy castle all in one afternoon!'
Gemma, mum to Daniel

Mercedes-Benz World
Brooklands Drive, Weybridge, KT13 0SL
0870 400 4000

'Essentially a large car showroom, but so much more! Entrance is free and there are three massive floors full of cars. Some of it is really just for sales, but there are lots of weird and wonderful cars to look at too. There are numerous exhibits about motoring which seem to change fairly often as well as quite a few vintage and special interest vehicles. Extremely helpful staff, baby changing facilities and a café or a restaurant for feeding time. When you have looked at everything else, you can watch the people in the driving school trying to keep their car on the track – surprisingly entertaining!'
Carla, mum to Ellis

'A great place to take children for a few hours on a rainy day. It is basically a huge car showroom, but children are allowed to sit in any car that is open. They can also watch cars on the test track, and join in with the Little Learners electric cars (fee payable). The staff are really friendly, and no one tries to sell you a car!'
Louise, mum to Joe, Emilia and Sam

Mizens Railway
Barrs Lane, Knaphill, GU21 2JW
www.mizensrailway.co.uk

'This miniature railway is a nice place to while away a couple of hours on a Sunday afternoon if you have Thomas the Tank Engine mad children (it is only open on Sundays).'
Leigh, mum to Ries and Elsa

Garden Centres

Badshot Lea Garden Centre
Badshot Lea Road, Farnham, GU9 9JX
01252 333666
www.squiresgardencentres.co.uk/garden-centre/badshot-lea

'*Badshot Lea Garden Centre* is a great place to while away a couple of hours with your tots. It has a great café with lots of yummy treats and a good selection for children. In the café there is a family room which has CBeebies on constantly, great if you are meeting a friend for coffee – I actually managed an uninterrupted conversation with my friend! Outside there is a small playground for children and

there is also a fantastic pets section with all the usual pets, plus a great reptile section and a talking parrot. The centre itself has a lovely shop selling great gifts, the Cook ready meals, arts and crafts stuff and a lovely selection of toys and books as well as garden stuff. They also often run extra activities for kids in the holidays. A real gem of a place.'
Joanne, mum to George

'There is quite a large café here with a designated kiddies room. They have CBeebies on and toys for the children. There is also a little terrace area and outdoor play area. The highlight was walking to the animal section and seeing all the fish, snakes, hamsters, rabbits and Bill the parrot! They also stock good children's toys – a perfect birthday present shopping trip!'
Tara, mum to Elliott

Clandon Park Garden Centre
Clandon Park, GU4 7RQ
01483 222925
www.clandonparkgardencentre.co.uk

'*Clandon Park* (also see page 30), with free parking, is a big house in beautiful grounds. They offer a children's trail and there are several good things to find including the Maori meeting house. Along the drive is a garden centre with a reptile house and goats. There is a café serving delicious food and you can sit outside under huge sunshades when it's warm. They also have baby changing facilities with a toilet in the same cubicle.'
Claire mum to Orson

'A little off the beaten track - once in West Clandon follow signs to *Clandon House, National Trust* property (see page 30). The garden centre can be found down a windy track. Friendly welcome, decent gift shop with cut-price toys and books, but best of all the lovely café with delicious homemade fare. Delicious homemade quiches, soups and specials of the day followed by scrummy cakes – all very reasonably priced. Kids menu a bit limited, but all the faves – including fishfingers, chicken nuggets, sausages, chips, beans etc. Nice spot for sitting outside when the weather is warmer. Opposite the garden centre is the reptile centre – fun for a look at some snakes, lizards and tropical fish. Combine with a trip to *West Clandon Playground* (see page 51).'
Ruth, mum to George and William

Notcutts Garden Centre and Pet Centre
Guildford Road, Cranleigh, GU6 8LT
01483 274222
www.notcutts.co.uk

'This is a good place to while away a few hours without spending money. It is a large garden centre complete with children's toys and books. My toddler enjoyed wandering round the outside plant area and also the pet centre which has a large indoor fish pond and a small range of animals including birds, fluffy bunnies and reptiles (we were able to go home and tell daddy we had seen a dragon). There is a restaurant selling homemade food and there are baby changing facilities, highchairs and a small play area in the restaurant.'
Tracy, mum to Eliza and Wilfred

Ripley Nurseries and Farm Shop
Portsmouth Road, Ripley, GU23 6EY
01483 225090
www.ripleynurseries.co.uk

'Small but worth a visit, *Ripley Nurseries* has a good selection of plants, a farm shop and a big car park (although it's gravelled, so not the easiest with a pram!). They're open seven days a week and staff are really knowledgeable and helpful. We're particular fans of the farm shop, which sells a wide selection of local fruit, vegetables, meat and other groceries. They have an award-winning gourmet burger van situated in the car park — worth a visit for this alone!'
Suzie, mum to Alexander

Woking Garden Centre
Egley Road, Mayford, GU22 0NH
01483 714861
www.thegardencentregroup.co.uk

'*Woking Garden Centre* has a huge selection of plants (vegetables, trees, herbs, flowers ...) and seeds, and all the equipment you could need for your garden. They also have a well-stocked pet shop inside, which is really handy, as well as a gift shop, café and garden furniture for sale. The staff are knowledgeable and friendly, and we sometimes go there just to have a look round and get some ideas. It's all on one level and easily accessible with a pram, plus the staff are happy to help you to your car if you haven't enough hands for all your purchases.'
Suzie, mum to Alexander

Leisure Centres

Guildford Spectrum
Parkway, GU1 1UP
01483 443322
www.guildfordspectrum.co.uk
(Also see *Guildford Spectrum* on page 109)

'The *Spectrum* is somewhat dated, but a fantastic source of entertainment. It offers a variety of sessions including *Toddler Splash* (see below), offering toddler (and parent) access to the leisure pool without the screams and splashing of larger children, as well as a variety of well-run lessons (see page 90), although these normally have a waiting list. Combine the attractions of the pool with the café (see page 136) and range of other facilities and you have a slightly tired but winning formula.'
Peter, dad to Thomas and Oliver

'It is worth picking up a holiday brochure from the *Spectrum* as they run various classes over the holidays, some of which are suitable for toddlers.'
Gemma, mum to Daniel

NCT Swimming – Tadpoles
Guildford Spectrum, Parkway, GU1 1UP
07850 025880
nctswimenquiry@live.co.uk
www.nct.org.uk/branches/guildford/events/baby-swimming/8
(Also see *Tadpoles* on page 6)

'These swimming sessions are great as, although they aren't lessons, it's a good way to get the babies into the water with someone who can give you tips for getting them used to it. You can take the baby in their car seat and there are poolside changing mats so the whole experience is made much easier. Anne, the lady who runs it is really nice and Caitlin loves going swimming, she's like a wind up frog!'
Miriam, mum to Caitlin

Toddler Splash
Guildford Spectrum, Parkway, GU1 1UP
01483 443322
www.guildfordspectrum.co.uk

'This is an ideal time to take your little one swimming at the *Spectrum* as the leisure

pool is reserved only for use by the under-fives and their grown-ups. There is something for all abilities with shallow pools to toddle through, a ship to play on with a small slide, and a deeper section for those who are confident in the water. They also open up one of the larger slides which you can use with your toddler on your lap. It usually runs in the school holidays but check the website as times tend to change.'
Gemma, mum to Daniel

Pool in the Park

Woking Park, Kingfield Road, Woking, GU22 9BA
01483 771122
www.woking.gov.uk/leisure/leisurecentrepool
(Also see *Pool in the Park* on page 109)

'If you fancy going slightly further afield, Woking Leisure Centre (*Pool in the Park*) has a great Lagoon pool and runs some fabulous parent and toddler splash sessions. It's nice and warm, and sessions are limited so it's never overcrowded (but you will need to pre-book). They have floats and aquatic toys as well as a wave machine and a nice slide for toddlers to safely slide down.
Changing facilities are clean and spacious and there is a really nice café which overlooks the pool. Prices are very reasonable and they do some very tasty children's lunches! There is plenty of parking outside and it is free for a limited period. At the bottom of the ramp that leads up to the complex is a nice park with a large array of swings and slides, and a pond to walk round if the weather is nice. All in all a good morning or afternoon's fun!
These are busy sessions so pre-booking is recommended.'
Nickkie, mum to Katie and Alice

Surrey Sports Park

University of Surrey, Richard Meyjes Road, GU2 7AD (for sat nav use GU2 7XX)
01483 689111
www.surreysportspark.co.uk

'This is a relatively new facility and although it doesn't have crèche facilities, their swimming pool is excellent. It is exceptionally clean in comparison to other pool facilities in the area and very reasonably priced. Under-fives are not charged for entry. It is a 50m pool which is often split for various activities. Sometimes when we go we have had to use the deep end, so would require you to have a child who is either a confident swimmer or ok with a floatation device. The times for how the pool is split are published well in advance on their website. They have a *Starbucks* café (see page 139) which is very roomy and the staff are always friendly

and courteous. *Surrey Sports Park* also has specific antenatal and postnatal exercise classes. Their swimming lessons are very popular and they lower the shallow end to an appropriate height for small children while the lessons are on. There are a good number of family changing rooms.'
Danielle, mum to Amelia

Something for Mum

Mummas and Beans
10 Queen Street, Godalming, GU7 1BD
01483 808842
www.mummasandbeans.co.uk
(Also see *Mummas and Beans* on page 137)

'Behind the café is a playroom and a beauty therapy room. This is great because you can either take the baby in with you or leave them playing in the crèche. Although the massage at *Mummas and Beans* is quite expensive, the woman who does the beauty treatments is really nice and it was the least painful waxing I've ever had!'
Amelia, mum to Ivy

'*Mummas and Beans* have a beauty room where you can get a massage or manicure and leave the baby in the crèche or take them in with you.'
Claire, mum to Orson

Alternatively ...
Of course, sometimes the best things to do are the simplest ...

'In our NCT group, we spend a lot of time going to each other's houses. It gives all the babies a chance to play with other toys without us having to buy loads. It's also a good, free activity and we know the changing facilities are clean and the refreshments are tasty.'
Cat, mum to Poppy

7. Soft Play

Tracy Liennard, mum to Eliza and Wilfred

Soft play is the answer to so many questions. How can I get my child to sleep as soon as his/her head hits the pillows? My child is bouncing off the walls, what can I do? It's raining, where can we go? Soft play will tire your children out, waste hours and hours of time, provide you with either hand-free time or at least an aerobic calorie burn as you follow your child up cushioned stairs, crawl through tunnels and whiz down slides. As your child gets older you get more freedom to enjoy friends' company or have a quiet cup of tea while watching your tearaways burn up all that energy. There are lots of really good soft plays around all offering your child (and you) a slightly different experience, so it is well worth visiting all of them.

Cranleigh Soft Play

Cranleigh Leisure Centre, Village Way, Cranleigh, GU6 8AF
01483 274400
www.dcleisurecentres.co.uk/centres/cranleigh-leisure-centre

'Located just inside the entrance to Cranleigh Leisure Centre and at just £3.10 per session, visits to *Cranleigh Soft Play* have become a regular fixture in my toddler's activity schedule. It's not huge, so can get busy at peak times, but if you go first thing in the morning (it opens at 9am), you'll often have the place to yourselves. On the positive side, its size also means your little one can't venture too far away from your line of sight. Beware of the entrance to the soft play area though, which doesn't have a gate, meaning the more adventurous can escape a little too easily if you're not paying attention!

As an added bonus, the leisure centre café serves a good range of drinks and snacks, and there are tables and chairs on the ground floor of the soft play area so you can have a civilised coffee while your little one plays. All in all, it's clean, not over-busy, good value for money and a great way of tiring out an energetic toddler.'
Jane, mum to Alex

SOFT PLAY

Farncombe Fun Zone
The Warehouse, Owen Road, Godalming, GU7 3AY
01483 861666
info@farncombefunzone.co.uk
www.farncombefunzone.co.uk

'A small soft play. Great for babies as there is a separate fully-enclosed area for under-ones (plus they enter for free). Not so good for small toddlers or early walkers as the rest of the soft play area involves climbing and playing at heights so is more suitable for two plus. Drinks and snacks available and there are plenty of highchairs. As this is a small soft play, adults can more easily sit and relax and watch their little ones run around without having to do so themselves. We held our NCT group first birthday party here.'
Vicky, mum to Amelia

'This is a small soft play over two levels. We held our son's second birthday party here and thought it was great for that age group. There are lots of tables and chairs for parents and there is a separate room where they put out the party food. Refreshments are available and there is a separate baby change area.'
Gemma, mum to Daniel

'You will come out smelling like a chip pan, but your little ones will have run/crawled themselves ragged and had a great time. There is small, separate area for crawlers/early walkers and big 'factory' of soft play for older ones. A café serves food and snacks with lots of tables, chairs and sofas for you to watch from.'
Carla, mum to Ellis

Farnham Leisure Centre
Dogflud Way, Farnham, GU9 7UD
01252 723208
www.dcleisurecentres.co.uk/centres/farnham-leisure-centre

'*Farnham Leisure Centre* run Funtime Gym, a drop-in session which is on most days. The hall is set up with a bouncy castle and various other play equipment as well as lots of ride-ons. A great rainy day activity.'
Joanne, mum to George

Fun in the Foam
Leatherhead and Dorking Gymnastics Club, Fetcham Grove, Guildford Road, Leatherhead, KT22 9BL
01372 377718
www.leatherhead-gymnastics.org.uk

SOFT PLAY

'There are four 45-minute sessions a day at this wonderful play space. Under-fives can hit the bouncy castle, trot along inclined benches, boing on trampolines and fling themselves from the asymmetric bars into the huge foam-block filled pit while parents enjoy the quiet backing track of S Club 7's finest work and resist the urge to flick-flack across the sprung floor. Much more civilised than the high-octane fun across the way at Leatherhead Leisure Centre's giant soft play area. Reception staff are hilariously grumpy, don't let them put you off. Changing facilities aren't great but you can easily make do.'
Katie, mum to Beth and Asa

Gym Jams
Normandy Village Hall, Manor Fruit Farm, Glaziers Lane, Normandy, GU3 2DE
07836 250099
info@gym-jams.co.uk
www.gym-jams.co.uk

'Sessions are held on a Wednesday and Friday, including school holidays. Places are limited so I find that it's best to book in advance, especially for the 9.30 session, but it does mean that it's never too crowded. It's held in a village hall and I like it as I can keep an eye on Daniel while chatting to friends. There is a bouncy castle, a ball pool, a trampoline, a balance beam and various other pieces of soft play equipment so there is plenty to keep the little ones entertained for the hour and a half session. Children get a drink and a biscuit and they do nice refreshments for the grown-ups. There is also baby changing and plenty of parking.'
Gemma, mum to Daniel

Madhatters Playhouse (previously Tiddler's Play Gym)
Jacobs Well Village Hall, Jacobs Well Road, GU4 7PD
07931 157769/07545 345277
madhattersplayhouse@gmail.com
www.madhattersplayhouse.co.uk

'This is a welcome addition to Jacobs Well and we love the fact that we can walk there rather than having to trek out in the car each time. There's a bouncy castle and plenty of soft play building blocks and a ball pool, plus a small sectioned-off baby area and a few ride-on bikes and little trampolines. I would say it's most suited to little crawlers rather than confident walkers as my eldest (almost three) got a little bored I think! They also serve drinks and snacks.'
Susan, mum to Thomas and Harry

SOFT PLAY

Piglets Play Centre
Burhill Road, Hersham, KT12 4BJ
01932 241323
info@pigletsplaycentre.co.uk
www.pigletsplaycentre.co.uk

'We discovered this place when we were invited to a second birthday party there. It took us less than 20 minutes to drive there from Guildford and I thought it was great for toddlers. There is a small soft play area with a fab slide, an area with lots of ride-ons, baby changing and refreshments. My son was 21 months old at the time and it kept him entertained for a good two hours and that was without going outside (it was a typical wet bank holiday Monday) where they also have an outdoor play area and farm animals.'
Gemma, mum to Daniel

'A tucked-away play centre with a good-sized outdoor area, including cute mini goats and pigs as well as a couple of bunnies. Lots of fun stuff for crawlers through to pre-schoolers, plus coffee, snacks and splendidly rubbishy magazines for grown-ups to flick through. Nice food for the kids, too. Can get very busy especially on rainy days, so it's worth getting there early if you can.'
Katie, mum to Beth and Asa

Purcy's Playroom
7th Woking Scout Hall, Woking, GU22 9BA
01483 346477
play@purcysplayroom.co.uk
www.purcysplayroom.co.uk

'*Purcy's Playroom* is a new concept in soft play offering pop-up soft play at numerous locations. They are currently at the venue above on Wednesdays and Fridays (9.30am-4.30pm) but check the website before you go to check where they are that week. There are different pods for toddlers and babies and the equipment is lovely and clean and new, especially the baby toys. Drinks, snacks and kids' lunchboxes are also available at a reasonable price. They also have a Facebook page and you can sign up to their weekly newsletter so you know where Purcy will be each week. My toddler loves saying "hello" to the Purcy signs every time we go! You can also hire their soft play equipment for special events and parties.'
Susan, mum to Thomas and Harry

Rokers Little Angels
Fairlands Farm, Holly Lane, Worplesdon, GU3 3PB

01483 232324
info@rokerslittleangels.co.uk
www.rokers.co.uk/littleangels
(Also see *Rokers Little Angels* on page 112)

'A large soft play – fantastic BUT it does get busier throughout the day and at week-ends. Loads of different soft play activities to keep your toddlers and small children amused. Ideal once your baby is walking. There is a separate toddler area but it is not enclosed so they can get out. A café on site to keep the adults sane and provide snacks for little ones once they have worn themselves out. Plenty of highchairs.'
Vicky, mum to Amelia

'A playcentre near Guildford with a large play frame and wavy slides for older children but also a bigger than usual area for the under-fours. There are tables and chairs in between the two areas so you can see both areas if you have multiple children with you. There is also the usual café, baby changing etc.'
Leigh, mum to Ries and Elsa

Rushmoor Gym
The Gymnastics Centre, Pool Road, Aldershot, GU11 3SN
01252 320888
info@rushgym.co.uk
www.rushgym.co.uk
(Also see *Rushmoor Gym* on page 87)

'*Rushmoor Gym* opens its doors to under-fives every day and lets them have a go on their gym equipment. They also have ride-ons and toddler play equipment. The area is vast so great for wearing out energetic toddlers.'
Joanne, mum to George

Specky's Pirate Ship
Guildford Spectrum, Parkway, GU1 1UP
01483 443322
www.guildfordspectrum.co.uk
(Also see *Guildford Spectrum* on page 60)

'This is a large soft play over several levels. Parents should go prepared to join in the fun as it's not possible to see all the levels from the seating area and younger toddlers tend to need a bit of help in some places. With three slides, a trampoline, ball pools, a tunnel to crawl through and lots of climbing there is plenty to do and we always have lots of fun here.'
Gemma, mum to Daniel

SOFT PLAY

Wendyhouse
44 Station Approach, West Byfleet, KT14 6NE
01932 344105
www.wendyhouseparty.co.uk
(Also see *Wendyhouse* on page 88)

'A great place for under-fives, there is a soft play area at the front with lots of different equipment: a trampoline, ball-pit, train tracks, doll's house, ride-in cars, etc. and very importantly coffee/tea/cake available for the grown-ups!'
Leigh, mum to Ries and Elsa

8. Classes and Courses
Claire West, mum to Orson

The number and range of activities on offer for your little one can be overwhelming, especially here in Guildford where there seem to be hundreds of things to do. This chapter looks at courses and classes that are either free, pay-as-you-go or can be bought in bulk.

You may be surprised to realise that so many of these classes are aimed at the younger audience and you may have thought that classes for children start as they become toddlers. However, there is a huge emphasis on the physical, mental and emotional needs of your baby and a great many activities have been designed by experts to aid your child's development. These would include baby massage, sensory play, baby signing sessions and music and rhyme groups where good leaders explain why they are encouraging certain actions and how the music helps baby's brain. In fact, there are plenty of developmental classes and courses in Guildford for all babies and children up to five years old. There are also swimming lessons which most of the children in our reviews absolutely adore, and storytelling groups that give carers a whole new source of inspiration.

Of course there is a huge social element to these classes, especially ones you attend regularly, and many carers admit they go to see their friends as much as because their baby or child loves it. Meeting other parents and carers is crucial as your friendship groups evolve throughout your child's first five years. For many of us moving to Guildford shortly before becoming parents, these groups are a lifeline to making friends. For others of us we find that friends without children are at work when we want to talk, and then there is the steady flow of carers heading back to work after maternity or paternity leave. Without these classes we would often find ourselves alone with a small child all day which, although lovely some of the time, can be too lonely all week.

CLASSES AND COURSES

So classes and courses may cost you financially, but often they pay back in many ways that make them more than worthwhile. Also it seems as though even if you just want to chill out and have fun, you're still doing the very best for your child, and for you – how fantastic! There are far too many to do them all and so we have collected recommendations by local parents and carers to help you out.

Busylizzy
G Live, London Road, GU1 2AA
Yoga Vita/Café Mila, 1 Angel Court, Godalming, GU7 1DT
www.busylizzy.co.uk

Some of the classes in this chapter and the next are run by *busylizzy*. This is a membership club providing a range of classes for parents/carers and children. Classes include yoga and Pilates for adults with soft mats for babies and toddlers, buggy fit and prenatal sessions. For children and babies there are music, crafts, dance and signing classes and they also hold social events and talks. Classes are held in *G Live* and there are several membership options. Here's what some local mums have to say about them:

'I discovered *busylizzy* whilst desperately searching for something to do with my little ones over the playgroup summer holidays and have been so pleased with it. We have things booked in to do all summer, and at £40 a month for a freedom pass covering both my boys, it's been really good value for our family. Our favourite sessions are French, Art and Pipsqueaks but there are loads of other options.'
Amy, mum to Thomas and Oliver

'Pros: classes are small (so instructors can pay more attention to your child), instructors are professional and enthusiastic, activities are well thought out, and toys/props are of good quality. Cons: Most baby classes are only 30 minutes long so depending on your baby's personality and level of curiosity, some sessions might not be stimulating enough. In my own experience baby classes are much better when your baby is not yet on the move (i.e. neither crawling nor walking), otherwise you'll spend a good part of the session chasing after him/her. Favourite classes: Little Pips Music and Mini Movers (there's a toddler version of this class called Mini Dancers) because it's 30 minutes of non-stop activities.'
Yuli, mum to Jonathan

'I joined *busylizzy* as a member as I wanted to have access to toddler activities in my local area and it appealed as it offers a wide range of classes at quality venues. The ability to either book on a pay-as-you go or monthly basis is fantastic as it gives you the flexibility to mix and match classes and find those that best suit your child. I've

busylizzy

Fitness and fun for mums and little ones

Award winning family members' club

- Classes
- Coffee mornings
- Guest speakers
- Meet like-minded new friends

www.busylizzy.co.uk

EAST SURREY BUSINESS AWARDS 2012 WINNER

been very impressed with the *busylizzy* website and the simplicity of the booking system, as you can easily see the class availability, book online and manage your schedule.'
Alison, mum to Lauren

'Busylizzy is THE BEST for everything – choice, value for money, fun, sharing and most of all the littl'uns LOVE LOVE LOVE it!! We especially like the Funtime French classes and the arts and crafts.'
Sarah, mum to twins Ruth and Curtis

Baby Massage and Yoga

Little Oasis Yoga
The Oasis, Shalford Infant School, Station Row, GU4 8BY
07825 321496
littleoasisyoga@gmail.com
www.littleoasisyoga.com

'I attended the *Little Oasis Yoga* with my youngest child Martha. I wanted to go somewhere that was friendly, welcoming and gave Martha and I some much needed quality time and we found all of this in Eve's class. The Oasis building is light, warm and clean. Eve starts the class with a lovely welcoming song that the children seemed to respond to despite being so young, and was understanding of baby's sleeping and feeding needs so was flexible in her approach which was much appreciated. The classes combine yoga for mummy with massage and yoga for the babies, and we were able to say if any of the positions were too uncomfortable post-delivery and Eve showed us how to adapt the positions so that we were not doing ourselves any harm. I would highly recommend this class as a chance to spend some time with your baby and do some exercise, as well as giving you the opportunity to meet other new mums so you can share experiences and maybe make a new friend or two!'
Karen, mum to Jack, Esme and Martha

'My daughter Molly and I started Eve's baby and yoga class when she was just four months old. The class is a relaxing, enjoyable and fun hour for us both. When she was little, Molly would be so relaxed by the end of the class she would fall asleep! Now she is one, she is thoroughly entertained joining me on the mat or flying through the air meeting the other babies. My eldest daughter Florence (four) is always welcome at the class (if she is not at pre-school). She brings her dolly to class and we all stretch together! Eve guides you through the class, explaining clearly, allowing you to do as much or a little as you can/want (especially having a

newborn and/or being sleep deprived!). Molly loves meeting and playing with the other babies and it is good to meet other local mums too!'
Emma, mum to Florence and Molly

Little Yogis
Busylizzy, G Live, London Road, GU1 2AA
www.busylizzy.co.uk

'We have been doing toddler yoga with *busylizzy* for just over six months and my son loves it. There is a range of yoga poses with fun games, pretending to be animals and learning about your body to music. It really is a fun class and I find that my son's co-ordination has really improved since he started. His favourite part is when they all get given a little pebble, have to make a wish and then put it in the magic water bowl. Adults are encouraged to join in too and it's for children aged two to five.'
Victoria, mum to Freddy

Rowan Perkin
07801 414435
rowan@rowanperkin.co.uk
www.rowanperkin.co.uk

'Rowan supports expectant parents (and babies) through their journey of parenthood, offering a wide range of holistic techniques including sleep workshops, baby massage, baby reflexology, baby yoga, HypnoBirthing and pregnancy massage. One of our NCT friends raved about Rowan's HypnoBirthing course, so a few of us went to her house to undertake a half-day baby reflexology course after the babies were born. Rowan was friendly and welcoming, putting us all (including babies) at ease straight away and making the course both fun and informative. On the way home and for the rest of that day, my baby was the happiest I'd seen him to that date (eight weeks old at the time) and we frequently use the techniques which were shown to us and given on a welcome handout!

As a result, our NCT group then booked Rowan to teach some of us baby massage. Instead of all driving to her house, Rowan came out to us and taught us in one of our homes, which was also lovely and very relaxing. The babies loved the massage and once again, Rowan taught us everything we needed to know but in a straightforward way that we could remember and use again.

Running courses in small groups means Rowan can tailor classes to suit the group, which is fantastic, and go at a pace which suits everyone. I would heartily recommend contacting Rowan to discuss anything you might be concerned about as we have all benefited through her courses from things she has taught us to cope with such as teething, colic, sore bellies, overtired babies ... Who doesn't need this kind of help?!?!'
Suzie, mum to Alexander

Willow Sanctuary
Watts Cottage, Jacobs Well Road, Jacobs Well, GU4 7PP
01483 824838
mich_morrow@hotmail.com
www.yoga-guildford.com
(Also see *Willow Sanctuary* on page 96)

'Two years on and we still do some of the rhymes that Michelle taught us in the baby yoga part of this course. The course, which needs to be booked in advance, runs for five weeks and is suitable for non-crawlers from six weeks old. Each class starts with baby yoga then moves on to baby massage before finishing with postnatal yoga for the mums. Don't worry if your baby needs feeding or changing during the session, it's all par for the course! Classes are held in a lovely location and I found them to be relaxing for both me and Daniel (he used to sleep very well afterwards!).'
Gemma, mum to Daniel

'The groups are kept small (six to eight people) and the atmosphere is relaxed, friendly and intimate.
Each class begins with some baby yoga moves, then moves onto massage allowing

you bonding time with your little one, and then time at the end for mums to do some stretching, relaxation, breathing and have 'time out' (baby allowing!). It doesn't matter if your baby decides they don't want to join in, chances are it'll happen to everyone at some stage, so you can just go at your own pace and feed or change your baby if you need to.

The course runs for about four to five weeks and is generally for babies from six weeks to just before the crawling stage.'

Carolyn, mum to Charlie

Dance, Drama and Sensory Play

Act One Adventures

Archies LaunchPad, The North Barn, Farnham, GU9 7PY
Mummas and Beans, 10 Queen Street, Godalming, GU7 1BD
07956 182488
joanne@actoneadventures.co.uk
www.actoneadventures.co.uk

'My recently turned two-year-old has really enjoyed his time in Jo's classes. Jo has a wonderful way of being able to include each child in the session by adapting her approach to suit the temperament and personality of each child as an individual. My little boy absorbs so much information during the sessions and often comes home singing a new song or discussing new shapes or wanting to carry on with an activity he has learnt during the session.'

Zoe, mum to Toby

'We attended one of the holiday sessions that Joanne runs and enjoyed it so much that we have signed up for regular classes next term. The session we went to was based around the 'We're Going on a Bear Hunt' book. After an active warm up, the children sat down to listen to the story. Then they were back on their feet to explore the ideas in the book, which involved imaginative play, lots of props and plenty of action. My son had only recently turned two when we went but it kept his attention for the most part which I was very impressed with!'

Gemma, mum to Daniel

Baby Picassos

Busylizzy, G Live, London Road, GU1 2AA
www.busylizzy.co.uk

'*Baby Picassos* is an excellent class. Great, casual agenda but lots of fun for babies and mums!'

Sarah, mum to Thomas

Baby Sensory
Bramley Village Hall, Hall Road, Bramley, GU5 0AX
Compton Village Hall, The Street, Compton, GU3 1EG
St John's Centre, 222 Epsom Road, Merrow, GU4 7AA
07582 209088
guildford@babysensory.co.uk
www.babysensory.com

'I take William to the Bramley class and although he's always loved it, he's got more out of it as he's got older. I find it great for getting ideas of what to do at home and for meeting other mums. There's a different theme each week with matching sensory experiences and there's loads of action songs so it is a really fun hour.'
Cat, mum to William

'We like *Baby Sensory* because as well as being a fun class to go to, she gives you ideas of how to play at home and what things to use to stimulate the babies' senses. Halfway through the class there's free time where the babies play with the huge selection of toys and equipment that she brings along.'
Buffy, mum to Hermione

'Each session has a theme and off we go! Paddling pools and paper fishes take us

to the beach, another week we are at the Rio carnival. There are lots of songs and musical instruments to fit with the themes, there is so much going on. There are two mini sessions within each class and free play (with a different set up every week – ball pools, tents, material, tea parties!) in the middle. We're in the older babies' group so most are raring to crawl about rather than sit with mummy, which is fine and, in fact, works really well for some activities. With so much going on a good nap is almost guaranteed.'
Carla, mum to Ellis

'My son George has been attending *Baby Sensory* in Bramley Village Hall for the last nine months. He started going at six months and he loves it! Every class he has been totally engaged – the music, the light shows, the balloons – so much goes into it! Cheryl is fantastic – so organised and the babies all adore her! I highly recommend it!'
Sally, mum to George

'My baby and I have been going to the *Baby Sensory* classes in Bramley since he was 18 weeks old. He's one next week and we both still love it. The class leader Cheryl is amazing and always makes the classes fun and gives you so many ideas for home. Jack smiles and laughs all the way through class and is always worn out afterwards. We love it so much that Cheryl is doing a sensory party for Jack's first birthday. We have done a lot of other classes and I have to say that this one is the best for length of class, price and entertainment. Will be sad to leave next term when Jack is too old!'
Jess, mum to Jack

'Of all the baby groups and classes I tried when my son was a baby, this was the undisputed favourite. It's aimed at babies from birth to 13 months, and the idea is to stimulate and support sensory development and communication skills through a range of activities. Even at just a few months old, my little one responded really well to the sensory stimulation, including fibre optic lights, bubbles, balloons, puppets and musical instruments, and the teacher built an impressive variety of activities into a 45 minute session.
The only drawbacks are that it's not suitable to take older children along to – making it tricky if you're a second time mum – and this area currently only offers classes for babies up to 13 months (although toddler sensory classes do run in other parts of the country).'
Jane, mum to Alex

'I attended two terms and the summer specials with my twins. They enjoyed it so much, we are all very sad that they are now too old to attend. One of the twins used

to squeak with excitement when we arrived at the class, as she knew what fun was going to be had! Every week a different theme to the class kept our interest. The toys for the free play time were fabulous, in excellent condition, and kept scrupulously clean. In short, I cannot recommend Cheryl Knight's classes highly enough!'
Miranda, mum to Tabitha and Evanthe

Disco Dudes and Divas
Busylizzy, G Live, London Road, GU1 2AA
www.busylizzy.co.uk

'We are going to *Disco Dudes and Divas* – my kids love it!'
Nicola, mum to Harry and Alice

Dynamic Tots
Burpham Primary School, Burpham Lane, Burpham, GU4 7LZ
Sutherland Memorial Hall, Clay Lane, Burpham, GU4 7LP
Worplesdon Memorial Hall, Perry Hill, Worplesdon, GU3 3RF
07766 077043/07753 985314
www.dynamicperformingarts.co.uk

'My daughter has attended Dynamic Performing Arts since she was two and a half and started in ballet tots. This is a fun and fab class to start girls and boys off with ballet! She has now started pre primary ballet and she still loves it, the classes are fun and run by friendly and enthusiastic people! I will be sending my other daughter there – I can't wait until she is old enough!'
Louise, mum to Lilly and Poppy

Gymboree
42 Station Approach, West Byfleet, KT14 6NE
01932 353313
westbyfleet@gymboree-uk.com
www.gymboree-uk.com

'This has been pricey but excellent. It's an activity class with parachute, sensory equipment, singing, signing, puppets and fibre optics which Ben is crazy about – or is it me – but most of the babies seem to like it and you can try a class for free.'
Louise, mum to Benjamin

Hip Hop Tots
Melody Bear Movement
Busylizzy, G Live, London Road, GU1 2AA
www.busylizzy.co.uk

'Our favourite classes are *Hip Hop Tots* and *Melody Bear*. The teacher is very calm, organised and the children are fully engaged. Theresa captures their imagination and interests brilliantly. The classes are really good fun and we are very lucky to have such a great opportunity to access these through *busylizzy*.'
Joanna, mum to Milly and Maisie

MAD Academy

The Masonic Hall, Ockford Road, Godalming, GU7 1RQ
Merrow Village Hall, 117 Epsom Road, GU1 2QY
The Spike, Warren Road, GU1 3JH
01252 326413
debs.newman@madacademy.com
www.madacademy.com

'*MAD Academy* is about music and movement and there are classes for babies, toddlers and pre-school children. I've been taking my son since he was about one, and although he doesn't always join in with everything (fortunately the lovely class teacher Jo is very relaxed about this!), I can tell he's picking it all up as he can always repeat the songs (and actions) word-for-word! It's a very varied class, including action songs, sound and colour recognition games, musical instruments, obstacle courses and, of course, the requisite bubbles which are always a favourite with all the kids! Classes last from 35-45 minutes depending on the age of the child. It's lively, energetic and lots of fun – well worth a try.'
Jane, mum to Alex

Music

Baby Bounce and Rhyme

Guildford Library, 77 North Street, GU1 4AL
0300 200 1001
libraries@surreycc.gov.uk
www.surreycc.gov.uk/people-and-community/libraries
(Also see *Blokes' Bounce and Rhyme* on page 108)

'This is a fantastic free singing session for babies. It is very popular and places are limited so get there early to avoid missing out. It is a good place to go to meet other mums and also to learn lots of action songs and nursery rhymes.'
Gemma, mum to Daniel

Little Surrey Songbirds

Millmead Centre, Bury Fields, GU2 4AZ

CLASSES AND COURSES

01483 283282
ruth@littlesongbirds.com
www.littlesongbirds.com

'My daughter and I have been attending *Little Songbirds* for many months and have loved every minute. The classes are very interactive, involving everybody, which has improved my daughter's confidence – she looks forward every week to going dancing with Ruth! Ruth the teacher is always full of energy and is very engaging which means the children never get restless. A great class!'
Ffion, mum to Bella

'This is a friendly music class which has a good mix of old favourites and new songs. Musical instruments and other props are used and the class also includes dancing, tickling and action songs. A free trial lesson is offered and I like that classes can be paid for on a pay-as-you-go basis, although you can also pay termly or half-termly for a discount.'
Gemma, mum to Daniel

'My daughter is two years and two months old and constantly sings Twinkle Twinkle Little Star. I decided we'd go along to Ruth's class to see if we couldn't widen my daughter's repertoire!
The class is very friendly and relaxed. Ruth has a great selection of games, musical instruments and of course song variety to offer to children of all pre-school ages. Whilst the odd child is often trying to escape or cause mayhem, we manage to bring everybody back to the circle and chirp out a few chords! There's a good balance of singing, dancing and fun to ensure that all the children are amused for the whole session.
My daughter took to the class immediately and now asks me when we're going to singing class again! It's great to finally hear her sing some other songs, but it does mean I go to bed at night with one of the favourites (usually the Roly Poly song) stuck in my head – hazard of being a parent I guess!'
Shelley, mum to Harriet and Hugo

Rhyme Time
Mummas and Beans, 10 Queen Street, Godalming, GU7 1BD
01483 808842
www.mummasandbeans.co.uk

'I have been to *Mummas and Beans* with Benjamin for *Rhyme Time* and he has really enjoyed it.'
Louise, mum to Benjamin

CLASSES AND COURSES

Sing a Song of Sixpence

St Albans Church Hall, Oak Hill, Wood Street Village, GU3 3ES
01483 870939
michaela@singasongofsixpence.co.uk
www.singasongofsixpence.co.uk

'My son and I have been going there for over a year, and we absolutely love it. It is a friendly and fun environment that is well organised. Michaela, who runs it, is a lovely person who really gets the children involved. I have made some fantastic new friends through this group and would thoroughly recommend it to all mums with babies or toddlers. It's just a shame we have to finish a year early due to work commitments, both myself and my son who is three will miss it dearly.'
Dawn, mum to Oliver

Squeakers Music

Busylizzy, G Live, London Road, GU1 2AA
www.busylizzy.co.uk

'We really like the new improved *Squeakers* class with Katie! The new timings work really well and I'm really pleased with the changes. I have talked to quite a few other mummies who also agree with me on this. The class is just that little bit longer now and really makes such a difference. We are planning to continue with the class indefinitely as Lily is still having a wonderful time – she spent the whole of last Thursday giggling through it which I take as a great sign! Long may *Squeakers* continue!'
Rochelle, mum to Lily

'I've been taking my little girl to the *Squeakers* music class at *G Live* in Guildford which she really enjoys.'
Alison, mum to Lauren

Zebedee's Music

St John's Centre, 222 Epsom Road, Merrow, GU4 7AA
01483 722434
amanda@zebedeesmusic.com
www.zebedeesmusic.com

'I would say this is better for babies who are nine months plus as we went when William was quite young and he couldn't really engage with it. However, it's great as there aren't many traditional nursery rhymes and she has quite a unique approach. There are lots of puppets and toys to represent what you are singing about. For

example if you sing about chickens and eggs, the children are given chickens and eggs to play with at the same time. There is a lot of learning involved and the toys all have to be put away by the children at the end, which I liked.'
Cat, mum to William

Birthday Parties

Exciting props, puppets and fun toys

Come and join in our fun music classes specially designed for children under 5

For more information or to book your **FREE** trial, please contact us:

info@zebedeesmusic.com

01483 27 27 51   *www.zebedeesmusic.com*

Signing

Baby Signing

Busylizzy, G Live, London Road, GU1 2AA
www.busylizzy.co.uk

'We love our signing class. Shona really engages Noah and we sing the songs all the way home in the car!'
Jenny, mum to Noah

TinyTalk

Jeffries Hall, Church of St Pius X, Laustan Close, Merrow, GU1 2TS
Oasis Room, Shalford Infants School, Station Row, Shalford, GU4 8BY
07973 937505
lyndsayh@tinytalk.co.uk
www.tinytalk.co.uk

CLASSES AND COURSES

'We love this class and have learnt lots of new rhymes, as well as learning the signs and fun ways to introduce them. Lyndsay keeps things moving quickly so the babies are never bored. Even when we are sitting, the more mobile ones are welcome to crawl or toddle about in this very relaxed group. There are quite a few in the class so I don't feel bad for my terrible singing voice. After lots of rhymes and some music making, there's a bit of free play and a cup of tea. It's a bit soon for our first sign, but we're taking it all in (well mummy is!), and Ellis is having lots of fun.'

Carla, mum to Ellis

'I have been interested in baby signing since my niece was a baby, so when Sam came along, we looked for a class that we could enrol in. The hour-long class is fun and fast paced and involves a mixture of floor play, signing to songs and reading stories. Sam loves it because the class is so action-packed, and I love it because it is a fun way to learn. Of course, the hard work is done at home. Sam is only four months, so it is still a bit early for him to sign, but he definitely already knows the sign for milk!!'

Nicky, mum to Sam

CLASSES AND COURSES

Sports

Ball Sports

Enjoy-a-Ball Sports Coaching
Various Woking locations
07843 283830
woking@enjoy-a-ball.com
www.enjoy-a-ball.com

'A non-competitive sports class for boys and girls from three years old which encourages their physical development but is more importantly lots of fun. It is lovely to watch them when they master a new skill like throwing and catching bean bags or winning games like 'smelly feet' or 'move-it, move-it'. Free trials are available so it's worth a go. The birthday parties they organise are also brilliant and you end up with a lot of very tired but happy children. Several people commented it that it was the best children's party they had been to after my son's fourth birthday party.'
Leigh, mum to Ries and Elsa

CLASSES AND COURSES

Little Kickers

Guildford Grove Primary School, Southway, GU2 8YD
Merrow Village Hall, 177 Epsom Road, GU1 2QY
01753 831902
pbrooker@littlekickers.co.uk
www.littlekickers.co.uk

'My husband has been taking my son for the past seven months to *Little Kickers.* He loves the group and the instructors are brilliant at teaching football games and helping improve your child's skills. We found that our son needed a bit of help in the first couple of months but as the months have gone by he now does the whole class unassisted and we just watch at the sidelines. It's a brilliant little group and the coaches make the classes really fun and varied each week. There is a good mixture of group games, individual skills, listening to instructions and of course, lots of fun! Would highly recommend.'
Victoria, mum to Freddy

'Liam started his *Little Kickers* football classes when he was 18 months old. From the very first lesson he and I were joyfully impressed! Coach Paul and Coach Nathan interact brilliantly with the kids which helps them stay engaged in all the learning fun. They learn and develop far more than to kick a ball into a goal; they learn about colours, develop their fine motor skills, balance, imaginary play and much more. I highly recommend *Little Kickers* in Guildford!'
Sonya, mum to Liam

'My son had spent months watching his older brother play football on a Saturday morning but was too young to join in the training and matches. I didn't have to look too far before finding *Little Kickers*. They focus on football skills and he always comes home having scored a goal for his team, Mighty Kickers, and can be just like his older brother. The games are really fun and different each week and the coaches full of enthusiasm. He loves it.'
Kathryn, mum to Nicole, William and Robert

'We love Coach Paul and his assistant coaches. Our two children have wildly different aptitudes for football but both were welcomed into the group, encouraged and supported. The little one, who is still attending the sessions, starts asking if it is time for *Little Kickers* a matter of hours after he finishes.'
Katie, mum to Beth and Asa

TENNIStogether

Rodborough School, Petworth Road, Milford, GU8 5BZ

CLASSES AND COURSES

01483 417592
www.TENNIStogether.com

'My daughter has recently started tennis lessons at the indoor tennis centre in Milford run by *TENNIStogether*. The centre is based at Rodborough School so it is really easy to get to and there is ample parking. There is a good lounge/viewing area so that younger children can sit with the adults and watch the lessons. Lessons start from age three upwards and the coaches are fantastic with the young children. They use the recommended court sizes and appropriate equipment for the children's age and ability. They follow the LTA and British Tennis Coaches Association recommendations for children to coach ratios. My daughter loves the lessons as they are really fun and the staff are friendly and helpful. They also take childcare vouchers which is an added bonus!'
Rebecca, mum to Isobel and George

Gymnastics

Gymnastics Factory
Pew Corner, Old Portsmouth Road, GU3 1LP
01483 455060
info@gymnasticsfactory.co.uk
www.gymnasticsfactory.co.uk
(Also see *Gymnastics Factory* on page 109)

'We have been going to *Gymnastics Factory* since my daughter was a four-month-old in the Caterpillars class where we enjoyed the variety of ways of encouraging tummy time, rolling and sensory stations. Now a very busy and active Beetle of 20 months we both look forward to our weekly class and Lyla claps wildly with excitement from the car seat when we pull up outside!
Gym Bug classes have helped her to develop not just physically but she is also learning through interaction with the other children, how to share (a work in progress!) and take turns. There is such a wide variety of equipment from the trampoline, trapeze into a foam pit, beams to balance on and bars to hang on. There are tunnels to crawl through and other soft play obstacles to challenge her and every week she hones in on a different piece of apparatus. There are energetic stations where she can run and jump and others that offer thought-provoking sensory elements and hand apparatus that test her co-ordination and patience.
The class combines free exploration and play with just the right amount of structure. We love the song and group time at the beginning and the bubbles and parachute at the end are also a big hit.
A visit to the coffee shop is a great way to build up friendships or have a sit down

after the class. In short, we have caught the 'gym bug' and can't wait to become a Dragonfly (age two to three).'
Kelly, mum to Lyla

'The *Gymnastics Factory* is a fantastic facility for toddlers. Although they run classes from six months I would say the benefit really comes into play from when a child first starts walking. My daughter joined *Gymnastics Factory* at two years and two months and has really excelled. In just six months she has learnt to jump properly, walk unaided across the beam and perform a forwards roll without help.
The team at *Gymnastics Factory* put safety first, which is not only great in the gym, but also translates to the park. Harriet will always turn round and climb down slowly rather than launch herself off something high. That said, her climbing is so much better now and she also climbs a lot higher!
It's definitely worth the money and they cater really well for siblings too. They have play pens on hand and baby toys to entertain 'littlies'.
They also do holiday sessions which can be a great benefit when all other classes have stopped!
You do have to pay £10 insurance for the year and £10 to join the British Gymnastics association, but *Gymnastics Factory* is the one expense I would recommend for all toddlers. It's also great for both boys and girls and saves you running from football to ballet! There's loads of free parking too!'
Shelley, mum to Harriet and Hugo

Kindergym

Woking Gymnastics Club, Kingfield Road, Woking, GU22 9AA
01483 771426
info@wokinggymnastics.co.uk
www.wokinggymnastics.co.uk

'*Kindergym* is a great introduction for little ones to the world of gymnastics. We often go to the pay-as- you-go unstructured sessions where little ones can work their way around the various pieces of gym equipment in a fun and relaxed, informal session. Each 45 minute session begins with a group song and a warm-up, and concludes with the coloured parachute, songs and sometimes bubbles. My little boy loves standing in line at the end for the ink stamps on his hands and feet!'
Susan, mum to Thomas and Harry

Rushmoor Gym

The Gymnastics Centre, Pool Road, Aldershot, GU11 3SN
01252 320888
info@rushgym.co.uk

www.rushgym.co.uk
(Also see *Rushmoor Gym* on page 67)

'A fabulous place for under-fives to let off some steam! Daily from 9.30-10.30am the Playgym class gives children an opportunity to explore the gym. My son was two when we first went, he absolutely loved running around, 'driving' the cars and jumping on the trampoline. It's quite busy but the gym is so big the only problem really is car park spaces!'
Tara, mum to Elliott

Wendyhouse
44 Station Approach, West Byfleet, KT14 6NE
01932 344105
www.wendyhouseparty.co.uk
(Also see *Wendyhouse* on page 68)

'In the back there is a hall where there are brilliant gym classes from 18 months upwards to really help the physical development of the children with a strong emphasis on fun. The staff are very friendly and have really helped my very shy daughter to come out of herself. In addition there are bouncy castle sessions, ball play and trampolining classes, with an external teacher coming in for Diddi Dance classes.'
Leigh, mum to Ries and Elsa

Martial Arts

Lil' Dragons
Guildford Academy of Martial Arts, 1 Ward Street, GU1 4LH
01483 568455
guildford_gbmaa@hotmail.co.uk
www.guildfordmartialarts.com

'Guildford Martial Arts run a programme for four- to six-year-olds called *Lil' Dragons*. It is a mixture of martial arts styles and the children get to take different coloured belts regularly. The sessions are very disciplined and the children are taught respect and self control along with the martial arts moves. They also have a section each week where the children are taught life skills such as healthy eating, stranger danger, memory skills etc. My son very much enjoys the sessions and we love the fact that they take an all-round approach to the sport. I know there have been parents who have sent their children who have conditions such as ADHD and autism and have been amazed by the impact the sessions have had on their children.'
Joanne, mum to George

'My daughter started with *Lil' Dragons* just after her fifth birthday and, nearly two years on, still loves it. The classes are for children between four and six and as well as giving them a grounding in martial arts techniques, they also encourage respect for others, self-discipline and thoughtfulness.

For a monthly payment, you can attend up to four classes a week – ideal for exhausting boisterous youngsters and there are regular gradings so they can work their way through the different coloured belts.'

Katie, mum to Beth and Asa

Swimming

(Also see *All About the NCT* and *Leisure Centres* in *Things to Do* for other swimming options)

Baby Swimming

Lockwood Centre, 9-13 Westfield Road, Slyfield Green, GU1 1RR
020 3176 5666
info@babyswimming.co.uk
www.babyswimming.co.uk
(Also see *Baby Swimming* on page 107)

'We take Ethan to the *Baby Swimming* classes in the hydrotherapy pool at Slyfield so the water is always really warm. Our teacher Jo amazingly remembers all the babies' names and he adores and always grins at her. From day one he's never cried and it's made him really confident in the water. She makes it fun and it's really well structured. At the start the babies are told "ready ... go" and then we pour water over their heads. Basically the class teaches them lots of signals like this to get used to. We are soon starting level three and feel that it's expensive but worth it.

When we were on holiday this summer, Ethan was really happy in the pool but a toddler near us was terrified of getting into the water. That's exactly why we started lessons early. Now Ethan is confident in the water, holds onto the edge and knows he has fun when he's in there.'

Cath, mum to Ethan

'Our swimming class is excellent and we have a wonderful teacher. William's been going since he was four months old, although I wouldn't take a baby any younger. There are changing mats around the edge of the pool so it's well set up for babies, but the adult facilities are pretty limited. There's a lot of repetition to reinforce learning which helped William get the hang of swimming underwater and understand the commands. They do a photo session at the end of the course and also offer catch-up sessions, so if you are away for a week you still get the number of classes you paid for.'

Cat, mum to William

'I highly recommend taking your baby to swimming classes. It's great fun for the baby and the parents (it's amazing to watch how much more confident the baby feels in the water week after week), and it fortifies the bond between you and your baby. We went to *Baby Swimming* in Guildford. Pros: Small size-class, good swimming pool with well-heated water, plenty of baby changing tables in the pool area, adult changing facilities/showers next to the pool area, teacher is knowledgeable and professional, class is well-planned according to each level, for those outside the pool there are plenty of chairs for partners/family to watch, there is an 'underwater photo shoot' session towards the end of each term with three print-outs for sale at £10 (pictures taken by the teacher). Cons: Room temperature in the pool area could be described as 'sauna-like' and although they offer catch-up sessions, they are not always available on weekends.'
Yuli, mum to Jonathan

'We started taking our son swimming from about three months old and he really loves it. His big smile makes the classes, which aren't that cheap, worthwhile. The pool at Slyfield is warm like a bath, almost too warm at times, and the classes are generally pretty small with no more than six to eight babies per group. The instructor we had was friendly and always explained things clearly which helped as I didn't take my son every week (so I often felt like I was the dunce of the class for not knowing what to do) but you soon pick it up. It can be a bit complicated to get changed but if you keep your child in his car seat while you get changed then take him into the pool area where there are changing tables it makes things easier. Afterwards, do the same in reverse so you minimise any time where your child could get cold.'
Duncan, dad to Daniel

Spectrum Swimming Classes
Parkway, GU1 1UP
01483 443322
www.*guildfordspectrum.co.uk*

'I have been taking my son here for almost a year. He enjoys the classes and the teachers are very good. The classes are split into ages and they run during term time.'
Tara, mum to Elliot

9. Prenatal and Postnatal Exercise

Claire West, mum to Orson

There are many classes in or around Guildford for parents and carers to get a workout without having to arrange childcare. These include buggy fit, pilates and yoga. These are mostly run during the day and designed for babies and children to attend. In fact sometimes the little ones provide the challenge either in the buggy as resistance to a jogging mum or as a weight to lift in pilates!

Buggy Exercise Classes

Buggy Bootcamp

Charterhouse Club, Duke's Drive, Charterhouse, Godalming, GU7 2RS
01483 239600
www.charterhouseclub.com

'If you have had your six-week check and are looking to get back to exercise (or start for the first time) *Buggy Bootcamp* in the stunning grounds of Charterhouse School could be for you. Breathing (or gasping) in lungfuls of fresh air while your little cherub sits quietly in the buggy marvelling at the strength in your triceps (thanks to hefting that car seat around) can give you a buzz that lasts all day. You don't need to be a member of the club and you don't need a fancy-pants buggy. What have you got to lose?'
Katie, mum to Beth and Asa

Buggy Fitness

Busylizzy, Stoke Park, GU1 1ER
www.busylizzy.co.uk

'I really enjoy the buggy fit class. It's great fun and Ian pitches it perfectly. My word, do my legs ache the next day though!'
Carly, mum to Henry

PRENATAL AND POSTNATAL EXERCISE

'This is a strenuous workout using the babies in buggies as weights and resistance when you're running. My baby loves being in the park watching the trees whizzing past and seeing me get more and more red faced!'
Claire, mum to Orson

Fit 4 Mum – Buggyfit
Painshill Park, Portsmouth Road, Cobham, KT11 1JE
www.fit4mum.com

'This class is awesome, the lady running it is so lovely and kind and will look after your baby if they are crying. It's £4.50 per session and pitched at the level of the mums who are there. She runs it at Painshill Park and also in Woking.'
Miriam, mum to Abigail

Pushy Mothers
Alice Holt Forest, Bucks Horn Oak, Farnham, GU10 4LS
Mummas and Beans, 10 Queen Street, Godalming, GU7 1BD
Shalford Park, Shalford Road, GU4 8BL
07702 854581
sophie@pushymothers.com
www.pushymothers.com

'I did this class when Ivy was three months old and thought it was brilliant. For me it was the beginning point for getting my fitness levels back up. It was also really good for meeting other new mums and going for a coffee afterwards.'
Amelia, mum to Ivy

'I first attended *Pushy Mothers* when Oscar was nine months old – I wish I had attended before this time but I could not find any information on such classes, but now there are many running!
I was never an exercise/gym person, so had not done any exercise for a good few years!! This I explained to Sophie and she was very kind and said to take it at my own pace. I really enjoyed my first class, and was able to keep up with the other mummies, but boy did I ache the next two days! I then attended every week in the wind, rain and snow up until I was 22 weeks pregnant with my second child. I had to stop as I started to get ligament pains from walking and was advised to stop by a physio.
I was then back when my little one was four and a half months old, with my double buggy doing double the work!! I really enjoy the classes, and at the end of each class I do feel I have had a workout. The classes are do-able, enjoyable, work all

those wobbly bits and just get you out of the house! It's also a bonus that you can have a chat with the other mummies about their little ones and share experiences that we are all going through or have been through. I feel it's a great way to exercise as you can take your little one along and they get to enjoy the fresh air and met new friends too.

I now recommend *Pushy Mothers* to all my friends who want to get out and exercise.'
Donna, mum to Oscar and Isla

'This class is for mums wanting to get back into shape with a gentle workout using the baby in the buggy as a weight.'
Claire, mum to Orson

Keep Fit

Baby Bounce
Holiday Inn, Egerton Road, GU2 7XZ
0871 9429036

'This class is a demanding workout for mums wanting to get back into shape. There are mats laid down for babies to lie on and the instructor is very baby-friendly. Go with a friend and take turns using the showers and have a coffee afterwards in their café.'

Claire, mum to Orson

Guildford Children's Centre
Hazel Avenue, Bellfields, GU1 1NR
01483 566589
admin@guildfordchildrenscentre.surrey.sch.uk
www.guildfordchildrenscentre.surrey.sch.uk
(Also see *Guildford Children's Centre* on pages 137 and 162)

'They offer several activities including a buggy walk which is great for meeting people and having a look around the local area, and a keep fit class. It's a great place to find out about other classes such as Zumba and they offer a crèche service while you're exercising.'
Claire, mum to Orson

Yoga and Pilates

The Pilates Way
Guildford Methodist Church, Woodbridge Road, GU1 4RG
Worplesdon Memorial Hall, Perry Hill, GU3 3RF
07803 128697
pilatesenquiries@hotmail.co.uk
www.the-pilates-way.co.uk

'I started antenatal Pilates at 12 weeks under instruction from Caroline Copp and have continued right up to my due date. Having never done Pilates before, I was a little apprehensive, but I found Caroline's style of teaching reassuring and extremely helpful. The groups are small, meaning you get a lot of one-to-one attention and they feel very personal, I've made several friends through the group who I am sure will be of great support once my little one arrives.
After the classes my body felt invigorated and they really helped to relieve any niggling aches and pains that begin to mount up as the weeks go on. I've not suffered with any significant back pain or complications, and am convinced that the exercises and techniques Caroline demonstrated are the reason for this. Pilates helps to strengthen your core and makes you more aware of your body – both of which are important in pregnancy. I cannot recommend Caroline's Antenatal Pilates course highly enough.'
Alexandra, mum to Meredith

'I started Pilates with *Pilates Way* at Worplesdon after the birth of my first child via c-section. I found this a great way to get back in shape and strengthen my stomach muscles. Once I fell pregnant with my second child I moved to their antenatal classes. These were brilliant and kept me fit throughout my whole pregnancy. My instructor Caroline was lovely and the class was really good fun and a good place to meet new mums-to-be as well!! My second birth was natural and a whole lot better than my first. I truly believe that Pilates had a great deal to do with this and I felt in better shape afterwards.'
Lucy, mum to Florence and Ava

'I attended Caroline's class after having my second baby. I can't recommend her classes highly enough. Having had a baby recently herself she knows what areas to focus on, and is very supportive. I had thought that my pelvic floor would never recover, but Caroline helped me to find it again!!'
Jo, mum to Jacob and Theo

PRENATAL AND POSTNATAL EXERCISE

Willow Sanctuary
Watts Cottage, Jacobs Well Road, Jacobs Well, GU4 7PP
01483 824838
mich_morrow@hotmail.com
www.yoga-guildford.com
(Also see *Willow Sanctuary* on page 74)

'I did the prenatal and postnatal/baby massage courses here. Michelle is lovely, leading you through gentle prenatal yoga, carefully adding options for later weeks! It was very useful for picking up tips for labour, meeting new people and then later for calming baby. Great relaxation.'
Carla, mum to Ellis

'Set in a purpose-built log cabin within the grounds of her home, Michelle offers antenatal, postnatal and general yoga for all and baby massage, and provides all the equipment such as massage oils, cushions, bean bags, mats etc. (you just need to bring a towel). I started going here when I was pregnant for antenatal yoga. I found it so helpful, it gave me my weekly fix of time out and me time, relaxing and calming me, and I've continued onto the postnatal course, as many mums often do.'
Carolyn, mum to Charlie

Yoga Mummy and Me
Busylizzy, G Live, London Road, GU1 2AA
www.busylizzy.co.uk

'After spending all week pushing the buggy and playing with the baby, it's great to have a really good stretch. Yoga is so good for detox and digestion and gets the lymphatic system going too. The class is in a lovely big room so we have space to move and the babies can lie on blankets or play with their toys, sometimes they even sleep through the class! It's so convenient to take them along and at the end we use them as weights and sing a song with them. The teacher is excellent and helps move you into position if you need it. She's also great at cheering up any grumbling babies. I always feel rejuvenated and Ethan always seems calm afterwards too.'
Cath, mum to Ethan

10. Playgroups
Ellie Atkins, mum to Gwen

Playgroups can provide a vital lifeline for parents. They are a great place to take babies, toddlers and pre-schoolers and a lovely place to meet other mums and to have a coffee and a chat. Generally they provide toys for babies and for older children and some arrange crafts, messy play, story times and singing. You don't have to be a mum either – dads, nannies and childminders are welcome at the groups too.

Parent and toddler groups are not registered with the local authority so your children remain your responsibility at all times during the session. Many are term time only and groups do come and go, so do check before you set off. In this chapter we've included all the reviews we've received and included local groups that we are aware of, in the quick reference guide, even where no review was submitted.

Quick Reference Guide to Playgroups:

Monday am
St Joseph's Mother and Toddler Group, Eastgate Gardens
Teddies Toddler Group, Emmanuel Church, Stoughton (Not 2nd Mondays, also Thursday pm)

Monday pm
St Paul's Bumps and Babes, Wood Street Village

Tuesday am
Chilworth Community Baby and Toddler Group, Chilworth
Getaway Club, Guildford Methodist Church, Woodbridge Road
Little Sunbeams Parent and Toddler Group, Manor Road Evangelical Church, Stoughton

PLAYGROUPS

St Francis Baby and Toddler Group, St Francis Church Hall, Beckingham Road
Stoke Toddler Group, St John's Church, Stirling Centre, Stoke Road
St Pius Baby and Toddler Group, Merrow
Teddy Bear Club, Guildford Park Church

Tuesday pm
Tuesday Club, Merrow Methodist Church

Wednesday am
ABC Playgroup, Christ Church Hall, Waterden Road
Evangelical Church Group, East Horsley
Queen Elizabeth Park Toddler Group, Stoughton (also pm)
Shalford Baby and Toddler Group, Shalford
St Nicolas Baby and Toddler Group, Bury Street
Tiny Treasures, Chertsey Street Baptist Church
Trinity Toddlers, Bramley

Wednesday pm
Queen Elizabeth Park Toddler Group, Stoughton (also am)

Thursday am
C.A.M.E.O (welcomes overseas families), Emmanuel Church, Stoughton (2nd and 4th Thursdays)
Guildford United Reform Church, Portsmouth Road
Little Lambs Toddler Group, Send Evangelical Church
New Horizons Toddler Group, St Peter's Church, Hazel Avenue
St Alban's Parent and Toddler Group, Wood Street Village
St Saviour's Baby and Toddler Groups, Woodbridge Road

Thursday pm
St John's Centre Parent and Toddler Group, Merrow
St Paul's Children's Centre Bumps and Babes, Tongham
Teddies Toddler Group, Emmanuel Church, Stoughton (also Monday am but not 2nd Mondays)

Friday am
All Saints' Baby and Toddler Group, Onslow Village
Caterpillar Café, Burpham
Millmead Baby and Toddler Group, Bury Fields

Playgroups

ABC Playgroup
Christ Church Hall, 23 Waterden Road, GU1 2AZ
01483 890456
jrvickerman@yahoo.co.uk
www.christchurchguildford.com
Wednesday 9.30-11.30am

'This group runs on Wednesdays from 9.30 to 11.30am during term time. There are separate areas for babies and toddlers and it has an outdoor play area too. The lady who does the rhymes session is very energetic and engaging. In general, it's been my experience with church groups that it doesn't matter which denomination they are, there isn't really any religious connotation to any of the activities they offer. That being said, this particular church group does have a 'bible story time' for toddlers, which is completely optional and it takes place in a separate room, outside the main hall area. Overall, I think this is a good playgroup to try.'
Yuli, mum to Jonathan

'Every Wednesday of school time from 9.30 to 11.30am. Children can play indoors (trains, Lego, kitchen, climbing, baby area) or outdoors if the weather is fine. A great place for children to play and mummies to meet and chat. For £1.50 you can also have a cup of tea/coffee and a biscuit along with rice cakes and breadsticks for the children. A well run, enjoyable playgroup.'
Tara, mum to Elliot

All Saints' Baby and Toddler Group
All Saints' Church, Vicarage Gate, Onslow Village, GU2 7QJ
07532 168473
office@allsaintschurchgfd.org.uk
www.allsaintschurchgfd.org.uk
Friday 9.30-11.00am

'*All Saints* is a traditional playgroup with an emphasis on nurturing and encouraging the children as individuals. It is run by a lovely group of local ladies, many of whom had children at the playgroup previously. I was worried about my son starting playgroup as he has always been quite shy but he has really blossomed and been so happy and I think that says it all about this lovely playgroup.'
Amy, mum to Thomas and Oliver

PLAYGROUPS

Caterpillar Café

Church of the Holy Spirit, New Inn Lane, Burpham, GU4 7HW
07774 171818
jclrunnacles@virginmedia.com
www.burphamchurch.org.uk
Friday 10-11.30am

'A large baby and toddler group with lots of activities – quiet corner, dressing up, crafts, toys etc. Hot drinks provided for the parents and towards the end all the children tidy up and are then given a drink and biscuit followed by a singing session. Nominal donation requested. My daughter loved coming here and there is so much to do that she never got bored. I also met a few local mums here who I see at the playground as well. Parking available.'
Vicky, mum to Amelia

'This is a toddler group in Burpham, which is really friendly and has lots of toys/ dressing-up clothes/arts and crafts etc to keep the children busy.'
Louise, mum to Joe, Emilia and Sam

Millmead Baby and Toddler Group

Millmead Centre, Bury Fields, GU2 4AZ
01483 575008
lisa.edwards@guildfordbaptist.org
www.guildfordbaptist.org/community/toddlers
Friday 10-11.30am

'This is a busy but well organised playgroup. There is a large room with lots of toys, a separate craft area, a small area for babies and a room where they hold story time and singing. The children get a drink and a biscuit at story time and they provide tea, coffee, biscuits and even cake for the grown-ups! There is plenty of space to park buggies and there is a baby changing table in the toilets.'
Gemma, mum to Daniel

Queen Elizabeth Park Toddler Group

New Life Baptist Church, Queen Elizabeth Park Centre, Railton Road, GU2 9JX
01483 235185
www.newlifebaptist.org.uk
Wednesday 9.30-11am and 1.30-3pm

'£1 entrance. This is a medium sized group with a small baby section and no waiting list. They have tea and cake for adults and singing and stories for the kids.'
Cat, mum to William

PLAYGROUPS

St Alban's Parent and Toddler Group

St Alban's Church Hall, Oak Hill, Wood Street Village, GU3 3ES
01483 233091
www.worplesdonparish.com/page/children-and-youth
Thursday 9.45-11.15am

'The Wood Street playgroup at St Alban's Church runs on term time Thursdays. There's a £1 donation and you get tea and coffee (if playgroups don't offer tea and coffee, I tend not to go!). There's a safe corner for non-walkers and you can take children from birth to five years old.'
Miriam, mum to Caitlin

St Joseph's Mother and Toddler Group

12 Eastgate Gardens, GU1 4AZ
01483 562704
stjo@guildfordcatholicchurches.co.uk
www.stjo-guildford.co.uk
Monday 10-11:30am

'They are on most Mondays during term times but occasionally it's closed when the hall is used for other church-related activities, so it's always better to get their term schedule at the door. There is a £2 donation paid when you come in which includes biscuits and coffee/tea as well as some snacks and refreshments for toddlers (I'm not familiar with these as I have a baby). There is an area right outside the main door to park buggies/strollers, as well as baby changing facilities. Toys are arranged more or less by age (for instance, there's a baby area with mainly soft toys, and a toddlers activities area for painting and craft-making). There is a short rhymes session at the end run by one of the volunteers. There are plenty of toys to play with and I think it's a great opportunity for kids and moms to make new friends. I have also found it useful for my baby to try out 'next stage' toys and see how he likes them before buying them myself.'
Yuli, mum to Jonathan

'A large group where babies are welcome and there is a good size baby area. It's great for toddlers and has bikes, a slide, painting, tunnels and singing at the end. They have tea and biscuits for parents and carers and it's just £2 entrance fee. There's no waiting list so just turn up.'
Cat, mum to William

St Paul's Children's Centre (Tongham) Bumps and Babes

St Alban's Church Hall, Oak Hill, Wood Street Village, GU3 3ES

PLAYGROUPS

Monday 1-2.30pm
St Paul's Children's Centre, Tongham, GU10 1EF
Thursday 1-2.30pm
www.stpauls.childrencentre.org

'It's a good laugh with a lovely bunch of people and when it was sunny we went out together afterwards. I think maybe I enjoy it even more than Caitlin does.'
Miriam, mum to Caitlin

St Saviour's Baby and Toddler Groups

St Saviour's Church, Woodbridge Road, GU1 4QD
01483 455333
www.st-saviours.org.uk
Thursday 10-11.30am

'The baby play area and toddlers area are separated (baby area is on the ground floor while toddlers' is on the first floor), which helps to keep the baby area more relaxed and quieter than in the mixed set-up. This group runs on Thursdays from 10am during term time. I have only experienced the baby area, but I've been told by other moms that the toddler area could get very hot. That is not an issue in the baby area, and volunteers supervising the group are approachable and engaged with all moms. On the down side, there is no rhyme session at the end (at least not when I've been), and the area to park buggies/strollers is a lot smaller than at other churches.'
Yuli, mum to Jonathan

'*St Saviour's* playgroup is a favourite of ours. It is really good for babies as there is a separate baby group downstairs which is a lot quieter than the busy toddler group upstairs. The room is split into two, with half for non crawlers, and the other half for crawlers and those who are walking but not yet ready to venture upstairs. The volunteers who run it are very friendly and tea, coffee and biscuits are provided.
The upstairs toddler group is more structured. There is a main room with a wide range of toys including ride-ons and a playhouse. There is also a small area for babies who are with older siblings. The back room, which tends to be a bit quieter, has a selection of toys, a book corner and a craft table with a different activity each week. Story time is held in the back room and is when the little ones get a drink and a biscuit. Refreshments are provided for the grown-ups in the main room after story time and there is a fun singing session at the end.'
Gemma, mum to Daniel

PLAYGROUPS

Teddies Toddler Group

Emmanuel Church, Shepherds Lane, Stoughton, GU2 9SJ
01483 567077
parish.office@emmanuelchurch.co.uk
www.emmanuelchurch.co.uk
Monday (except 2nd in each month) 10-11.30am
Thursday 1-2.30pm

'We have been going to *Teddies* playgroup at Emmanuel Church for a year now and really enjoy it. It's £1 per visit but you do get a tea/coffee and a biscuit. It's a lovely group in the church hall with a good variety of toys for babies and toddlers. They do a craft activity every week and also a story/singalong session whilst the toddlers get juice and a biscuit. It's very friendly and they also do end of term parties which are really fun! The only downside is the long waiting list.'
Victoria, mum to Freddy

Tiny Treasures

Chertsey Street Baptist Church, Chertsey Street, GU1 4HL
01483 300238
www.csbc.org.uk
Wednesday 10-11.30am

'It's the best organised playgroup I've ever been to. There's a corner for non crawlers and the room is pretty big with loads of toys and some bouncers so you can bring children of different ages. They have a 'bikes in the hall' half hour of chaos and they block the babies off with chairs. You can get a coffee and they provide drinks and snacks for the children. At the end you all tidy up and have story and songs. It's just magic and a really inclusive atmosphere.'
Miriam, mum to Caitlin

Trinity Toddlers

Holy Trinity Church Hall, High Street, Bramley, GU5 0HD
01483 890042
office@holytrinitybramley.org.uk
www.holytrinitybramley.org.uk
Wednesday 10-11.30am

'Bramley playgroup runs every Wednesday, even in the holidays from 10-11.30am and is held in the church hall to the side of the Holy Trinity Church in Bramley. Jill runs the group, she is very friendly and in fact everyone there welcomes you warmly. The toys are lovely and well looked after, coffee is decent

and everyone gets a biscuit! It's a great way to meet mums in the villages.'
Shelley, mum to Harriet and Hugo

Play and Learn Sessions

Play and Learn sessions are held at the various *Children's Centres* (see page 160).
The days and times do tend to change from one term to the next so it is worth
ringing or checking the website before you go. Unlike playgroups where you can
drop in at any time, these sessions tend to get full quickly and so it is best to arrive
on time or even earlier to guarantee a place. In addition to the sessions below, the
Boxgrove Children's Centre runs a *Play and Learn* session in Ripley fortnightly on
a Thursday morning, the *Guildford Children's Centre* runs sessions in some of the
villages and it's also worth knowing that the various *Children's Centres* run other
groups for mothers and babies which tend to be organised according to the age of
the children. Further details can be found on their websites.

Hazel Avenue Play and Learn
Guildford Children's Centre, Hazel Avenue, Bellfields, GU1 1NR
01483 566589
admin@guildfordchildrenscentre.surrey.sch.uk
www.guildfordchildrenscentre.surrey.sch.uk
Thursday 11am-12.30pm; 2.30-4pm
(Also see *Guildford Children's Centre* on pages 93, 137 and 162)

'My son and I enjoy going to the *Play and Learn* sessions. Lots of toys, including
some lovely sensory ones, for him to investigate and lots of mums for me to talk
to. The ladies that run it are always happy to chat. Get there early to make sure you
get a place as we have been a couple of times to find it full and they were unable to
take more babies. There is a good café in the building doing coffee and sandwiches
for very reasonable prices so it's nice to grab a quick bite or slurp first.'
Carla, mum to Ellis

'With a good variety of toys and books there is plenty to amuse little ones. If the
weather is hot and sunny then they put up gazebos to provide some shade in the
garden. There is also a sandpit outside which my son loves. Places are limited and
it can get full very quickly but if you turn up and find there are no spaces left then
there is always the café or the book corner to occupy your little ones for a while.'
Gemma, mum to Daniel

'We have been going to *Play and Learn* at Bellfields *Children's Centre* since Orson
was about four months old although it's set up for younger babies too. They have

different sessions depending on how old your child is but we've only been to the pre-crawlers group. There are loads of toys and other stimulating equipment and the babies lie, sit and roll around amongst it all. It's very unstructured although there are staff on hand to offer advice or make suggestions.

They are really lovely and amazingly remember the babies' names despite seeing so many every day. I must admit we largely go because I enjoy meeting new people and seeing friends as it's a great source of information and conversation with other new mums. I also find it one of the nicest places to go without knowing anyone as you can always get talking to someone.

We tend to get there early and head to the café for a super cheap cup of tea and homemade cake or some lunch as they do sandwiches and jacket potatoes too. There's an outside area by the café for when it's sunny and if it's really hot, the *Play and Learn* group move outside onto the grass too although there's not loads of shade there. It's all free which is fantastic and the *Children's Centre* is a brilliant source of information so worth going to at any time.'

Claire, mum to Orson

'Hazel Avenue *Children's Centre* does a couple of *Play and Learn* sessions in the week. There are a range of activities that change each week including painting and playing with playdough. There are also a range of toys to play with, a play kitchen area (which my daughter loves) a dressing-up area and a large outdoor play area as well as other mums to talk to. The staff are always really nice and the session ends with some fruit and juice at the table followed by a few songs (some of which were new to me). The Sure Start centre itself has a café on site to visit if you want to after your *Play and Learn* session. The food is basic (sandwiches, jacket potatoes) but very reasonably priced.'

Tracy, mum to Eliza and Wilfred

The Spinney Play and Learn

St Francis Church Hall, Beckingham Road, GU2 8BU
01483 510570
childrenscentre@guildfordgrove.surrey.sch.uk
www.thespinneycc.org.uk/Play+and+Learn
Monday 9.30-11.00am
(other sessions run at *The Spinney* throughout the week)
(Also see *The Spinney Children's Centre* on page 164)

'Friendly welcoming drop-in session. Well set up with different activities for babies and toddlers such as messy play, crafts, ride-on toys, singing and a baby area. The room is not too big so a good session to go to with a toddler and small baby.'

Alexa, mum to Iyla and Grace

PLAYGROUPS

York Road Play and Learn
Guildford Children's Centre, York Road, GU1 4DU
01483 561652
info@guildfordchildrenscentre.surrey.sch.uk
www.guildfordchildrenscentre.surrey.sch.uk
Tuesday 9.15-10.45am
Friday 1.30-3pm

'The York Road *Play and Learn* group is a great place to meet other new mums. I got some excellent advice when I was there recently so I'm really glad I went even though Cherie is too small to actually play.'
Florence, mum to Cherie

11. Ideas for Dads

Alistair Gerrard, dad to William

After five days of freedom at work, all too often the weekends seem to consist of two Daddy Days, especially when it's mummy's turn to lie-in.

So what do you do with a toddler once breakfast is over? A trip round the local supermarket may be essential, but it doesn't feel like the highest quality experience in terms of parenting; sacrificing a box of grapes for the desired peace to food shop and avoiding the toy aisle. Hopefully a few of the destinations outlined below might help. Of course, dads are welcome at other places mentioned in this book, but the following have been recommended by dads themselves.

Classes and Things to Do

Baby Swimming
Lockwood Centre, 9-13 Westfield Road, Slyfield Green, GU1 1RR
020 3176 5666
info@babyswimming.co.uk
www.babyswimming.co.uk
(Also see *Baby Swimming* on page 89)

'*Baby Swimming* offer lessons in Slyfield which are pricey, but no more than anyone else offering lessons and the teacher we have is brilliant. She remembers all the babies' names after just one session and they all seem to respond really well to her. My baby loves swimming and from the very start was happy to go under water so we're really pleased. Make sure you time their food and sleep though as even a half hour lesson exhausts babies and makes them ravenous. This is a great activity for dads to bond with their babies and I love the time we spend together while mum has a lie-in. Doing it alone can be challenging though, so here are my top tips:
1) Get both of you into swimming trunks (and baby into the swim nappy) while you're still at home.

IDEAS FOR DADS

2) Have the towels, nappy and change of clothes at the top of the bag for a quick getaway.

3) Take the car seat in so you can get changed easily.

4) Take food supplies as swimming is hungry work.'

Ross, dad to Orson

'Matthew has been attending since he was around three months old and is now just over two. The classes have really built his confidence in and around water, which has been noticeable around other children on holidays. The pool at Guildford is probably actually a bit too warm and the classes don't come cheap (currently around £120 for ten weeks of lessons) but 90% of the babies and toddlers we have shared classes with have visibly loved the time they spend in the pool. By the higher levels, there is some repetition which is probably only noticed by parents, and does seem to continue to build confidence in the children. The balance of most of the classes we have attended have been pretty even between mums and dads and if anything slightly more dads. Overall if you can spare the time and the cash then it can be really rewarding.'

Andy, dad to Matthew

Blokes' Bounce and Rhyme

Guildford Library, 77 North Street, GU1 4AL

0300 200 1001

libraries@surreycc.gov.uk

www.surreycc.gov.uk/people-and-community/libraries

(Also see *Baby Bounce and Rhyme* on page 79)

'If you want to hear a bunch of slightly knackered/hungover blokes singing nursery rhymes out of tune, then these monthly Saturday morning sessions for dads are for you. The kids seem to like it and it's a good chance to have a bit of bonding time with your child. If you don't know all the words, they provide songsheets for you to mumble along to! And it's free.'

Duncan, dad to Daniel

Boogie Babies

Surrey Sports Park, University of Surrey, Richard Meyjes Road, GU2 7AD (for sat nav use GU2 7XX)

01483 689111

www.surreysportspark.co.uk

'I used to take my son to the *Surrey Sports Park* (see page 61) on Monday mornings for *Boogie Babies*, a fun class which combines songs and actions with informal play

time with toys. The teacher was very enthusiastic. My son was only nine months old when we went and I think he was probably a bit young to really enjoy the class but he did like watching the older kids dance and perform the actions in time to the music. It costs £4 a time which I think was a little expensive.'
Duncan, dad to Daniel

Guildford Spectrum
Parkway, GU1 1UP
01483 443322
www.guildfordspectrum.co.uk
(Also see *Guildford Spectrum* on page 60)

'Great for swimming on a Saturday morning.'
Alex, dad to Ellie and Lizzie

Gymnastics Factory
Pew Corner, Old Portsmouth Road, GU3 1LP
01483 455060
info@gymnasticsfactory.co.uk
www.gymnasticsfactory.co.uk
(Also see *Gymnastics Factory* on page 86)

'The *Gymnastics Factory* is a large, very well-appointed gym which runs classes for babies, pre-walkers, toddlers and upwards. The staff take the time to explain different toys and apparatus and there's a focus on different aspects like climbing or balance each week. It's a safe environment where kids have lots of space to explore and try out different apparatus.'
Duncan, dad to Daniel

Pool in the Park
Woking Park, Kingfield Road, Woking, GU22 9BA
01483 771122
www.woking.gov.uk/leisure/leisurecentrepool
(Also see *Pool in the Park* on page 61)

'Good swimming but the pool can become full quickly. An excellent park outside.'
Alex, dad to Ellie and Lizzie

IDEAS FOR DADS

Parks, Walks and Woodlands

Cutmill Ponds
Suffield Lane, Puttenham, GU3 1BG

'A tranquil old mill pond to walk around, with a few ducks to point at. One part of the path is quite muddy and may require carrying your toddler but it's otherwise very pleasant and easy walking.'
Matthew, dad to Thomas

Millmead Lock
(behind *Debenhams* and the Yvonne Arnaud Theatre), GU1 3UU
(Also see *Millmead Lock* on pages 42 and 123)

'Ideal on a sunny day for an impromptu picnic, with lots of ducks to point and shout at. Plenty of open space to run about and some shallow water for the brave toddler to dip a toe into. Occasional narrow boats come by and negotiate the lock. Plenty of trees for shade but it can get busy quickly.'
Angus, dad to the tribe

Newlands Corner
Shere Road, GU4 8SE
(Also see *Newlands Corner* on page 43)

'Great for a walk with stunning views. Not ideal for footballing due to the distinct slope (seemed like a good idea initially), and beware of rabbit holes. Open space one way, wooded on the way back. A lovely café at the end for drinks and snacks to reward any toddler.'
Alex, dad to Edward

St John's Lye
St John's, Woking, GU21 7SW

'This is our local village green and hosts a good playground that is always busy. But the *Lye* itself offers much more, with ample open grassy space for any number of activities, such as football. There is a second field beyond which backs on to the mainline railway from London to Weymouth (with five other W's on the line – can you name them?), allowing for some train-spotting. There are a number of accessible wooded areas with mostly easy paths and a stream that is sadly a little too shallow (so far) for Pooh Sticks. Finally, the village has a Co-op/Spar for drinks and ice creams.'
Alistair, dad to William

IDEAS FOR DADS

Stoke Park
Stoke Road, GU1 1EP
(Also see *Stoke Park* on page 36, 39 and 48)

'Not just the large open space opposite the *Spectrum* (see pages 60 and 109), but loads more. Park in Nightingale Road and you will also have access to an excellent play area, a boating pond and large paddling pool, and loads more.'
Dominic, dad to Olivia

'*Stoke Park* is a relatively hidden gem and the playground is an absolute highlight. It offers more than the traditional range of swings and slides, with a superb climbing frame/raised walkway and a helter-skelter style slide. Elsewhere within the park is a duck pond, a large paddling pool (only open at certain times of the year) an outdoor café and a large number of shaded grass areas for those warm, sunny days. Parking is generally easy, either on Nightingale Road or in the *Stoke Park* car park just off it. Other items that appeal include the, typically, four trains an hour that run just past, overlooking the park – perfect for toddler visibility.'
Peter, dad to Thomas and Oliver

Sutherland Memorial Park
Clay Lane, Burpham, GU4 7JU
(Also see *Sutherland Memorial Park* on page 50)

'The playground is split into two, one section primarily for toddlers and one for slightly older children. There are a number of climbing frames and several swings and slides all set within a large area of grass with some trees and shrubs, which is good if your child is in a mood to explore rather than play. Daniel has been enjoying the toddler section since before he could walk and is now up and down the various climbing frames and slides like he was born to it. It's one of our favourite places to let him burn off his abundant energy.'
Stephen, dad to Daniel

Virginia Water Lake
London Road, Virginia Water, GU25 4QF
www.theroyallandscape.co.uk/gardens-and-landscape/virginia-water
(Also see *Virginia Water Lake* on page 46)

'A huge lake to walk around with many features to explore. The full circumnavigation is about 4.5 miles, so may be a bit far for everyone. But plenty of opportunities to stop and have drinks and ice creams. Be aware that the car park is ticketed but there is a cash point at the petrol station opposite.'
Dominic, dad to Kitty

Soft Play

Rokers Little Angels

Fairlands Farm, Holly Lane, Worplesdon, GU3 3PB
01483 232324
www.rokers.co.uk/littleangels
(Also see *Rokers Little Angels* on page 66)

'Be prepared for the wall of noise to hit you as you enter this soft play centre. There are areas for under-fours and over-fours where you can let your child roam free and burn off their excess energy. You just need to keep an eye on them as some of the older kids can be a bit over-enthusiastic in the ball pit – just make sure they don't dive in without checking if your baby's underneath.'
Duncan, dad to Daniel

'An excellent indoor soft play centre with a decent amount of area for adults to sit and have a coffee whilst toddlers burn off energy exploring. Some peculiar health and safety rules regarding the age restrictions for the slide but otherwise excellent. Staff very friendly and accommodating.'
Duncan, dad to Marcus

'*Little Angels* is a large soft play centre split into two parts. There is a small area for the crawlers and toddlers and a larger section for the older children. The really nice thing about the crawler and toddler area is that it's a proper little soft play and not just an area with assorted blocks as some others tend to be. There is a café so parents and children can both get food or drinks, although if the weather is bad it can be hard to get a table as it gets very busy.'
Stephen, dad to Daniel

12. Shopping
Gemma Gregson, mum to Daniel

As busy parents, we are on a constant mission to find things that make our lives easier. The internet has revolutionised the way we shop, offering everything from books and clothes to groceries. In addition, in today's world of austerity measures, secondhand shopping is firmly back on the agenda. This chapter is not intended to be a complete A-Z of shopping in Guildford; we can all take a walk around Guildford town centre and see what it has to offer. Instead we have focussed on those places that save us time and/or money.

Online Shopping

As busy parents with limited time, the internet offers a low stress alternative to tackling the town centre with little ones and buggies. Most shops now have their own website and mail order services and some businesses offer online shopping only. We have included some of our favourites below. There is also a list of online retailers that sell nappies in the *Services* chapter.

Amazon
www.amazon.co.uk

'When a trip to the shops is just a little bit too much effort, and you actually have no idea which shops sell what you are looking for, *Amazon* is great. The prices are usually slightly cheaper than the high street and they stock everything you could need for baby, from nappies to some weird and wonderful gadgets. I have found they are usually the cheapest place for branded nappies, but make sure to factor in delivery charges.'
Carla, mum to Ellis

'*Amazon* is my favourite online shop. I buy all sorts from *Amazon* and it has seen us

113

through every stage of Daniel's life. From when he was a newborn and we needed changing mats and top and tail bowls, through to the weaning stage when we bought books, bibs and highchairs, and finally to the toddler stage when we are buying trikes and garden toys. It is also great for birthday presents and the reviews are particularly useful in helping to find a toy or book that is loved by little ones.'
Gemma, mum to Daniel

Books for Bugs
www.booksforbugs.co.uk

'Are you looking for good quality books for your children, but fed up of the huge price of children's books? Are you looking to write reviews of your favourite books and win vouchers for doing so? Are you keen to support a hardworking local mum (of three!) who is working to get children reading quality books for great prices? If the answer to any of these is 'yes', I would heartily recommend *Books for Bugs*. They have a really simple plan – to buy quality children's books in bulk and sell them online at just £2.99 each, regardless of the RRP. When we found out about this great deal, I organised a large delivery for our NCT group and the books arrived really quickly, in perfect quality, at £2.99 each – the books are new, there's no catch and

we shall be ordering time and time again as our bug grows into new titles. Happy reading!!'
Suzie, mum to Alexander

The Book People
www.thebookpeople.co.uk

'*The Book People* often have some fantastic deals on children's books and I have bought some really good value box-sets from them.'
Gemma, mum to Daniel

Kiddicare
www.kiddicare.com

'*Kiddicare* sell all sorts including baby equipment, nursery furniture and toys. I find their prices to be good (they claim they are never beaten on price) and they offer free next working day delivery (conditions apply) with a one hour time slot (they text you on the morning with a time and if it's no good then you rearrange for another day) which is really handy. They also seem to stock most brands and I like reading the reviews before I buy.'
Gemma, mum to Daniel

Red House
www.redhouse.co.uk

'We are huge fans of *Red House* for children's books. All the classics are there as well as current hits and more unusual titles. You can search by age, price or category which I really like too. The discounts are amazing, you can do it online and delivery is free if you spend £15. We usually find it hard to spend that much despite buying loads so we team up with friends and buy together.'
Claire, mum to Orson

Riverford
www.riverford.co.uk

'Gorgeous organic food boxes, not too turnip-heavy. Excellent service, including a wonderful database of recipes should you run out of inspiration. On the rare occasions I'm struggling to get excited about the contents of my weekly veg box, I remind myself what a truly ethically thoughtful company *Riverford* is, get the peeler out and make soup.'
Katie, mum to Beth and Asa

Pay-at-pump Petrol Stations

With thanks to *Suzie, mum to Alexander*. The following petrol stations have facilities enabling you to pay at the pump with your credit or debit card rather than having to go into the shop to pay:

Brooklands Tesco
Barnes Wallis Drive, Weybridge, KT13 0XF
www.tesco.com

Esso
Bellfields, GU1 1NH
Hogs Back, GU10 1EU
www.essofuelfinder.com

Secondhand Shopping

Don't forget that the NCT also run secondhand sales. More details on the hugely popular *NCT Nearly New Sales* can be found in the *All About the NCT* chapter on page 11.

Freecycle
my.freecycle.org

'Online the best place for secondhand baby gear is *Freecycle* where people offer things they no longer want, often in great condition, for free. We got our buggy, most of my maternity clothes and his baby clothes, a travel steriliser, plastic balls to play with and loads of other things. We have also got rid of things this way such as two wardrobes, drawers and a tent.'
Claire, mum to Orson

Gumtree
www.gumtree.com

'*Gumtree* is a great place to pick up bargains such as baby equipment, clothes and toys. You can search by area e.g. Guildford, or by item, so if you desperately want a baby bath and are willing to travel, you can search for the item and then decide which to contact. The difference with eBay is that the price is fixed and you can go and see the item before deciding if you want it. We got our pram, activity jumper, stair gate and baby carrier all on *Gumtree* at hugely reduced prices. As usual with

secondhand baby gear (in our experience), it is all in amazingly good condition.'
Claire, mum to Orson

Nuthill Fruit Farm Car Boot Sale
Nuthill Fruit Farm, London Road, GU23 7LW (3 miles north of Guildford on the southbound carriageway of the A3)
01798 865703
www.facebook.com/Nuthillcarbootsale

'We go here most Sundays – not only does our baby enjoy the fresh air in his pram, but it's a great place to pick up a bargain, from children's clothes and toys, to furniture, bikes and plants. It's easy to access, just off the southbound carriageway of the A3, there's plenty of parking, and it's only £1 to go and look at all the stalls. If you're looking to sell things (and there's a great demand for secondhand children's clothes, books and toys), you'll find a ready market and it's £10 to sell.
Running weekly from the first Sunday in April to the last in October, from 7:30am to 1pm, and with plenty of refreshments on site, it's a fun way to spend a Sunday morning.'
Tony, dad to Alexander

Oxfam Bookshop
220 High Street, GU1 3JD
01483 504257

'Before my son was born, I collected books from here with a compulsion. Now I don't have time for my books, but I find great ones for him at a fraction of the full price, still in good condition.'
Carla, mum to Ellis

Rethink Mental Illness
Queen Street, Godalming, GU7 1BD

'Godalming has several charity shops which always have a great range of children's clothes, toys and books. For the best selection of secondhand books at amazing prices, go to the *Rethink Mental Illness* charity bookshop on Queen Street.'
Claire, mum to Orson

Supermarket Shopping

A trip to the supermarket can be an activity for little ones in itself. Pick a time when your child is not going to be tired or hungry, go armed with two lists (one for you and one for them to get them involved) and a snack for your little one (to save them wanting to sample everything that goes in the trolley) and don't forget some patience and a sense of humour, and supermarket shopping can be both educational for your child and rewarding for you.

However, a trip round the supermarket with little ones in tow can also be very challenging, which is where online grocery shopping comes in. Shopping can be done from the comfort of your own home at a time that suits you and some even have apps which makes it even easier as they save having to switch on the laptop. Delivery times and prices differ between supermarkets, and can vary depending on your postcode, so have a read of the reviews then check out the websites for yourselves and find one that suits you.

Ocado
www.ocado.com

'They sell the Derma H20 Water Wipes which is why I use them as I can't find these as cheap anywhere else. They use a lot of Waitrose products including the essentials range, but not exclusively.'
Claire, mum to Orson

Sainsbury's
www.sainsburys.co.uk

'I am a recent convert to online grocery shopping and it is a real time saver. *Sainsbury's* offer one hour time slots and have always delivered when they say they will. Once logged in, their website remembers your usuals making the shopping really quick to do. I have to confess, however, that I still like to pop into the store itself especially for fresh fruit and veg and they also do a good range of children's clothes in the store in Burpham.'
Gemma, mum to Daniel

Tesco
www.tesco.com

'*Tesco* online shop is a really easy way to get your groceries. It has some really handy features to help you do the shop quickly, including listing items you recently bought (either online or in the shop) and items you always buy. It also tells you when there are deals on items you want and lets you know if you've missed a promotion. They will deliver with or without bags (and you get green Clubcard points if you don't have bags). The delivery drivers are always helpful and my deliveries have always been within the time slot. When I was pregnant or holding a small baby they always took the shopping right into my kitchen. If they have

to substitute an item it is always bagged separately so you can find it easily, and then decide if you want it or not. I also like that you can go back and amend your order after you have done the shopping so you can add all the items you forgot. Delivery costs vary, so I usually go for 7pm or later as these tend to be cheaper. Mondays and Saturdays tend to be more expensive but other days are usually ok. At Christmas time you need to book a delivery slot early as they do get full up quickly.'
Ellie, mum to Gwen

Waitrose
www.waitrose.com

'Having tried the online delivery service for a number of supermarkets, I find that *Waitrose* online offers a little bit extra. Delivery is always free and, although you can only book a two hour time slot over 24 hours in advance, if you need your shop sooner you can select to collect your order in store instead. When you order you can write notes for the picker per item and, on delivery, the driver will take your shopping directly to your kitchen. Perhaps the best thing is that if they have to give you any substitutions you only pay for the cheaper item so you often get a better product for a lower price.'
Claire, mum to Sam

13. A Trip into Guildford Town Centre
Gemma Gregson, mum to Daniel

Once children come along, a trip into Guildford becomes a very different experience. Gone are the days when a day out in town included a leisurely look round the shops, trying things on, perhaps going back to the shop you started in. Instead, it becomes something more akin to a military operation. The list is made, shops identified and the items in question are picked up in the minimal amount of time before your little ones become bored or need feeding or changing. With this in mind, we have included ideas for keeping your children entertained while on a shopping trip along with those all-important facilities. Why not have a look at the *Cafés and Bars* and *Restaurants and Pubs* chapters for refreshment ideas too.

Entertainment

Allen House Grounds
Eastgate Gardens, GU1 4AZ

'We like to pop by here on the way back to York Road car park which is just next door. There is no play equipment but my son enjoys running around the open space in the gardens and watching the school kids play football in the tennis courts. It's an ideal place to let your little one stretch their legs before being bundled back into their car seat.'
Gemma, mum to Daniel

Cotswold Outdoor
2-3 Friary Street, GU1 4EH

'In a recent quest for a new jacket, this store proved to be a real find for keeping William amused whilst I shopped. There was a funny-terrain boot-testing hill to

clamber over, a tent to hide in, and plenty of space to run around. The only slight concern is the staircase.'
Alistair, dad to William

Foxenden Quarry Playground
York Road, GU1 4DN
(Also see *Foxenden Quarry Playground* on page 47)

'York Road next to St Joseph's Church – there's a playground next to the multi-storey car park for a quick play after going round the shops although it is more suited to slightly older children.'
Claire, mum to Orson

Guildford Castle
Castle Street, GU1 3UQ

'Although there's not a lot of room to run about, this is a lovely spot for a picnic – great while you are looking for a break from shopping. The flowers are always beautiful and colourful. There are lots of different parts to the gardens with the shadier bowling greens at the top and the walls around the Castle Keep at the bottom. Most seem to be accessible with a buggy by finding the right slopes. There are some hidden treasures so keep your eyes out for all the interesting little fountains and inscriptions, as well as our favourite shady spot, the 'Alice' garden.'
Carla, mum to Ellis

Guildford Library
77 North Street, GU1 4AL
(Also see *Guildford Library* on page 167)

'This is one of our favourite places to go when in town. It's great for letting little ones out of the buggy for a while and in addition to the large selection of children's books to read there or borrow, they have a table with paper and crayons.'
Gemma, mum to Daniel

House of Fraser
105 High Street, GU1 3DU

'There is a fish tank next to the steps on the ground floor as you come in from the High Street. There is a ramp on the left-hand side if you want to get closer with the buggy.'
Gemma, mum to Daniel

A TRIP INTO GUILDFORD TOWN CENTRE

Kiddy Cars

The Friary Centre, North Street, GU1 4YT

'*Kiddy Cars* are push-along cars which are available from the Concierge on the ground floor. My daughter and her friends love going for a 'drive' in these – hiring one makes shopping fun and what's more, they can be hired free of charge. (Note – terms and conditions apply). Good baby changing facilities too.'
Vicky, mum to Amelia

Millmead Lock

(behind *Debenhams* and the Yvonne Arnaud Theatre), GU1 3UU
(Also see *Millmead Lock* on pages 42 and 110)

'This is a nice place to go for a break from shopping or to while away a Sunday afternoon. My son enjoys seeing all the ducks and watching the boats go through the lock.'
Gemma, mum to Daniel

'An ever-popular spot, but beware the geese. Were they so pushy when we were kids? Once you have depleted your bread supplies you can spend ages catching up with the action at the lock. I think I find it even more intriguing than the kids do.'
Katie, mum to Beth and Asa

A TRIP INTO GUILDFORD TOWN CENTRE

Playworld
The Friary Centre, North Street, GU1 4YT

'A great and very cheap way to while away wet mornings with your toddlers or placate them after a shopping trip. *Playworld* is a children's soft play area located on first floor outside Primark. Although the area is enclosed, there is no gate at the entrance, so parents need to be on their guard to make sure little ones do not escape!'
Vicky, mum to Amelia

Ride-ons
The Entertainer, 13 North Street, GU1 4AF
Trotters, Unit 6, White Lion Walk, GU1 3DN

'We can't go into town now without Daniel asking to go on the Postman Pat ride-on outside The Entertainer toy shop. Luckily he just likes to sit on it rather than have a proper ride otherwise it would cost me a fortune! There is also a ride-on outside *Trotters* which he enjoys.'
Gemma, mum to Daniel

Trotters
Unit 6, White Lion Walk, GU1 3DN
(Also see *Trotters* on page 165)

'When my son was younger we used to drop by here just to have a look at the fish. It's also one of my favourite shops for presents for nieces and nephews, as it has a different selection to the norm and they do some lovely toys and books.'
Gemma, mum to Daniel

Waterstones
71-73 High Street, GU1 3DY
(Also see *Waterstones* on page 55)

'We find popping into *Waterstones* whilst on a high street shopping trip is a welcome distraction for a bored toddler. At the back of the store on the ground floor is the kids' area with a brilliant fish tank and lots of comfy seats for them to look at books and play with toys. Just enough entertainment to buy you a bit more time walking round the shops, and I usually end up buying at least one book!'
Susan, mum to Thomas and Harry

Toilets and Baby Changing
Carla Applegate, mum to Ellis

One of the most practical and useful aspects of previous editions of *Tots About Town* seemed to be the section on feeding, baby changing and toilet facilities in Guildford.

Suddenly taking a small person around town brings a whole new experience of the town centre: places you never knew existed pop up before your eyes in a Harry Potter-esque way. Most important is finding somewhere comfortable and clean to feed or change your baby. A few years later it turns into a mission to find the nearest toilet in the shortest possible time, multiple times during the same trip. And, of course, there's mum! A toilet that you can bring a buggy into becomes the nirvana of toilets.

Once we started making these lists, it appeared there are in fact an abundance of these facilities in Guildford.

One more thing, if you have a smart phone, check out the NCT babychanging app. It's free to download and you can add to it to help create a database of changing facilities. It can prove handy, especially if you are visiting an unfamiliar town.

A TRIP INTO GUILDFORD TOWN CENTRE

Quick Babychange Checklist:
Boots
Debenhams
The Friary – ground floor
The Friary – second floor
G Live
House of Fraser
Jojo Maman Bébé
M&S
Mothercare
Next
Waterstones
WHSmith

Boots
85-89 High Street, GU1 3DS

'Behind the stairs by the baby section is a small room with changing stations and a bottle warmer.'
Claire, mum to Orson

Debenhams
Millbrook, GU1 3UU

'There are a couple of changing bays at the back of second floor, and a small room for feeding tucked just behind.'
Carla, mum to Ellis

The Friary Centre
North Street, GU1 4YT

'On the ground and top floors there are separate rooms with basic changing facilities. They also have chairs for feeding babies. In the toilets downstairs there's one with a child toilet and sink in the same cubicle as the adult one.'
Claire, mum to Orson

G Live
London Road, GU1 2AA

'*G Live* has several excellent baby change toilets which are five star. Totally worth

the walk uphill from town for these clean, spacious toilets with large changing tables. The hand dryers are pretty powerful and always make Ethan jump but that's a small price to pay. There is also a little café in reception and there are toys for toddlers to play with while you relax on the big sofas.'
Cath, mum to Ethan

House of Fraser
105 High Street, GU1 3DU

'*House of Fraser* has excellent changing facilities. Babies will be occupied watching themselves in the mirror while you change them! There is a toilet for adults in there as well, with plenty of room for the pushchair. Use the cleverly concealed ramps to get around the shop. There is a fair bit of space for pushchairs in the in-store *Caffè Nero* (see page 129) too if you or little one are in need of refreshment.'
Carla, mum to Ellis

'There is a toilet with a changing station next to the *Caffè Nero* (see page 129) on the first floor. It's usually clean and has a big mirror and wall stickers to keep babies interested and still (ish!).'
Claire, mum to Orson

Jojo Maman Bébé
19 Swan Lane, GU1 4EQ

'Near the back there is a baby changing room and toilet.'
Claire, mum to Orson

Mothercare
12C North Street, GU1 4AF

'In the back corner is a room with two changing stations. There is seating for feeding babies and also a bottle warmer.'
Claire, mum to Orson

Next
Unit 1-2 White Lion Walk, GU1 3DU

'There is a baby changing table in the toilets on the 1st floor (behind the tills in the women's department).'
Gemma, mum to Daniel

A TRIP INTO GUILDFORD TOWN CENTRE

Waterstones
71-73 High Street, GU1 3DY

'There is a baby changing table in the disabled toilet on the ground floor at the back of the shop.'
Gemma, mum to Daniel

WHSmith
56 High Street, GU1 3ES

'There is a baby changing table in the disabled toilet on the first floor, opposite the escalator. The lift is near the back of the shop.'
Gemma, mum to Daniel

York Road Car Park
York Road, GU1 4EA

'*York Road Car Park* (the 11th level) has one toilet that is big enough to take a pushchair into. There is no baby changing as such but there is space by the sink to change a nappy if desperate.'
Gemma, mum to Daniel

14. Cafés and Bars
Susan Sanderson, mum to Thomas and Harry

Walk down Guildford High Street on any Saturday morning with a buggy or straggling toddler in tow, and you'll quickly see that most of your fellow shoppers are on the same mission: to find a decent café that will provide us with that crucial caffeine and sugar kick to get us through the weekend whilst keeping our little ones suitably amused!

Since joining the parenthood club I sometimes look back longingly on our BK (before kids) days when we could take a slow meander to the shops and while away the morning (and usually our hangovers!) with a nice cup of something hot and a read of the papers. In fact, my husband and I only recently had a long discussion trying to remember exactly how did we spend our weekends and how did we possibly fill two whole days without any work?! I wouldn't change what we have now for the world and three years on we have learnt that it is even possible to still enjoy those trips out for coffee and cake with little people in tow – you just need to know where to go and where to avoid. I hope this chapter gives you a few helpful tips and maybe even gives you a few new places to try – enjoy!

Guildford Town Centre

Caffè Nero
House of Fraser, 105 High Street, GU1 3DU
01483 511192
www.caffenero.com

'I was so pleased when I found *Caffè Nero* in *House of Fraser* when my son was very small. It's located on the second floor and you need to take the lift and the disabled ramp to get to it. It is large enough to have your pram by your table and it's never usually too busy, so if your baby is sleeping then you don't have to put them in a

highchair as you can normally just wheel the pram next to you. I have also breastfed here as there are sofas and you can be really discreet. The staff don't bat an eyelid as it's mainly full of mums and babies (we did a few NCT meet ups here in the early days). The staff are friendly and will bring your drinks/food over to you if you don't have enough hands. The café is also located right next to the baby change (see page 127) so it's really convenient. I found that this is one of the only places in Guildford where you can actually relax with your baby in the pram knowing that if you need it then all facilities are under one roof.'
Victoria, mum to Freddy

'The café is situated on the first floor of *House of Fraser*, and can be directly reached via the lift by the cosmetics on the ground floor (there are other lifts but you will need to manoeuvre your way through the store!). This is a great place to stop if you want to have a quick drink or light bite, while feeding your baby. There is plenty of space for pushchairs and feeding, and the baby change (see page 127) is next to the café.'
Jacinta, mum to Sophia and Annabelle

'*Caffè Nero* on the first floor of *House of Fraser* is child-friendly and has highchairs. There are usually several babies in there and it feels comfortable breastfeeding. They do a reward card so you can get a free drink after several visits. It is also really close to the toilets and baby change station (see page 127).'
Claire, mum to Orson

Caracoli
Steamer Trading Cookshop, 168 High Street, GU1 3HS
01483 346060
www.caracoli.co.uk

'I didn't realise this café existed but it's a really bright, light café with a lift for buggy access. The salad was delicious and there's an amazing looking selection of cakes. A good sized disabled toilet with nappy changing station and spare wipes is also a bonus and makes it all round kiddy-friendly.'
Liz, mum to Charlie

'If you actually like coffee, forget those buckets of soupy froth you get from the big chains and head to *Caracoli*. There are fabulous views from its location at the top of the Steamer Trading Cook Shop, the coffee comes in sensible sized cups, is expertly made and can all too easily be accompanied by one of their excellent bakewell slices, or you could try the passion fruit and orange cake. If you are proper hungry, investigate the sausage rolls and scotch eggs. You won't be disappointed. On Saturdays they sell a range of artisan breads from De Gustibus. Service is impeccable and the loos immaculate!'
Katie, mum to Beth and Asa

'Fantastic food and a lovely atmosphere. Busy and buzzy, but relaxed, with some nice views over Guildford. They are very happy to have children there, the staff were excellent with little ones and they have a lovely changing area, complete with wipes in case you are running short!'
Carla, mum to Ellis

The Continental Café
6b Tunsgate Square, GU1 3QZ
01483 303619
www.tunsgate.co.uk

'A bit of a hidden gem as far as I'm concerned. If you are in need of a place to feed your little one or grab a much-needed shot of caffeine yourself, the *Continental Café* is worth considering. As well as the area inside the coffee shop, there is a large dining area in the main atrium in Tunsgate that customers can use. The benefit of this is space! Room for you, little one, a buggy, tons of shopping and a highchair (which they have available for you to borrow) without squashing up against your neighbours. The highchairs have little tables on them and are adjustable so great for smaller babies too. The café has baby change facilities and the staff seem friendly and relaxed. I felt comfortable breastfeeding here. Oh and the scones are amazing!!'
Debs, mum to Amelie-Rose

'This café is in the atrium area of the Tunsgate Centre so not only is it bright and airy but there is loads of space for pushchairs. Additionally there are lots of highchairs available so it's a great place to get together with a group of mums if little ones need feeding.'
Vicky, mum to Amelia

Costa
www.costa.co.uk
Unit 34, The Friary Centre, GU1 4YW

'Despite my general indignation at the price of coffee in all cafés these days, a visit to *Costa* has become a pre-requisite of any shopping trip with my son since he discovered the 'babycinno'. At just 50p for either a warm milk or mini hot chocolate, it's better value than the grown-ups' version and well worth it for the opportunity it gives you to indulge in a coffee of your own and to put your feet up for a few minutes. The staff in our favourite *Costa* – the one in Guildford Friary opposite Primark – are generally very helpful and friendly, and if you can get a seat in the 'outside' area then you and your kids can happily while away the time with a good dose of people-watching!'
Jane, mum to Alex

Unit 1, Guildford Station, GU1 4UT

'We have stopped here a couple of times with our toddler whilst waiting for our train to arrive. There is ample space for pushchairs and a variety of seating including comfy chairs. There were highchairs at the back and also baby changing in the disabled loo. There is the usual array of cakes and biscuits and also sandwiches and paninis. I also noticed they did fruit which was great. The coffee is good – nice and strong to get you through the day. There is also a variety of juices for little ones. You can, of course, take away if you are in a rush. The staff are friendly.'
Victoria, mum to Freddy

Debenhams Restaurant
Millbrook, GU1 3UU (ground floor at the rear)

'This is a great and under-utilised restaurant and they really cater for little ones. There is sufficient space for pushchairs, they have plenty of highchairs plus they have a bottle warmer and a microwave for warming up jars of food (hidden behind one of the pillars). Additionally they have everything you might need to feed your little ones – jars of baby food and toddler/child lunch boxes are available to purchase and they provide throwaway cardboard bowls with a bib and a wipe inside. Baby

change facilities are on the second floor. Tip: don't bother trying to struggle and enter via the front doors if you have a pram or pushchair, walk along the side of the building to the first set of doors on the right where there is a button operated, automated door for wheelchair access.'
Vicky, mum to Amelia

'Debenhams has a restaurant on the ground floor overlooking the river. There is an outside area but inside is huge so plenty of space for buggies. They do a wide range of food, drink and cakes and have highchairs for children. They offer a bottle warming service and there are always a few babies and children in there. Despite being an open and bright area, it does feel comfortable to breastfeed there.'
Claire, mum to Orson

The Garden Room
Sydenham Road, GU1 3RT
01483 577696
www.gardenroomguildford.com

'A small café which has limited space for pushchairs and only ONE highchair. Lovely place to go for lunch if you are with the family but forget it if you are out with other friends with babies/toddlers.'
Vicky, mum to Amelia

G Live
London Road, GU1 2AA
01483 739040
www.glive.co.uk
(Also see *G Live* on page 53)

'There is a huge amount of space in the reception/café area of *G Live* so it's perfect to meet other friends with buggies or toddlers. They have some toys in the corner to keep little ones amused and nice big sofas to relax on. The café is a bit limited but they do the usual selection of drinks and a couple of snacks for kids and grown-ups. One main selling point is the spacious, clean changing rooms (see page 126) and toilets which make the walk to the top of town completely worth it.'
Claire, mum to Orson

Pret a Manger
26/28 Swan Lane, GU1 4EQ
020 7932 5371
www.pret.com

CAFÉS AND BARS

'*Pret* in Swan Lane is bigger than it looks and there's a baby change station in one of the toilets.'
Claire, mum to Orson

Riverbank Café Bar
Yvonne Arnaud Theatre, Millbrook, GU1 3UX
01483 440000
www.yvonne-arnaud.co.uk/food-and-drink

'Enjoy your lunch on the riverbank! The food is good and there is quite a range for a small café. There are plenty of highchairs and there ought to be enough to distract little ones. The interior is a bit dated, but if you are looking for somewhere quieter, this is great.'
Carla, mum to Ellis

The Slug and Lettuce
North Street, GU1 4AA
01483 561660
www.slugandlettuce.co.uk/guildford

'This is a great place to meet up with a group of mums and babies. It is quiet during the day and there is plenty of space for pushchairs. My NCT group used to meet here every week for coffee and bacon sandwiches, until our babies needed more entertainment than a bar could provide! We used to feel comfortable breastfeeding in here and the staff were friendly, one week they even went out and bought decaf coffee especially for us. The disabled toilet has a baby changing table in it, although you may need to ask for the key to open it.'
Gemma, mum to Daniel

Starbucks
195 High Street, GU1 3AW
01483 454385
www.starbucks.co.uk

'We went in here because *Caffè Nero* up the road doesn't have baby change facilities and this was the closest place I could think of for coffee. Actually pleasantly surprised. There is a decent amount of space and adequate baby change facilities, and a really handy location.'
Suzie, mum to Alexander

CAFÉS AND BARS

Tea Terrace
House of Fraser, 105 High Street, GU1 3DU
0844 800 3730

'The *Tea Terrace* is a lovely place to stop off for a speciality tea and delicious cake when you are out and about in the town centre with little ones. Its location on the top floor of *House of Fraser* is very convenient and the lifts to the rear of the store take you and your buggy directly there. The baby changing and toilet facilities are very good and are located near the lift. There is a great sofa/armchair area and also a seated restaurant area – some tables have fantastic views!
It's not just tea and cake on offer, they have a simple but tasty lunch menu and the food on the children's menu is good quality. There is also a wine list for those looking for a glass of wine with lunch!
Highchairs are available and during the week there is usually plenty of space to keep a buggy by the sofa/table, however weekends can be busy therefore you may be asked to leave your buggy at the side of the room if your child is big enough to use a highchair.'
Zoe, mum to Imogen

'*House of Fraser* has a lovely light restaurant at the very top of the store. There are some tables outdoors in good weather and there's a great garden up there on the terrace. They have good baby changing facilities and there are sofas that you can relax on with plenty of space for buggies.'
Cath, mum to Ethan

Out of Town

The Bramley Café
4a High Street, Bramley, GU5 0HB
07504 792597
www.bramleycafe.com

'I don't often say this about cafés, but their food is amazing – it's so fresh and they offer a great range. It is a good place to go after *Baby Sensory* (see page 76) and the outdoor space is lovely when it's sunny. In fact it's almost worth the drive and is easy enough to find parking nearby.'
Cath, mum to Ethan

Café Mila
1 Angel Court, Godalming, GU7 1DT
07788 219373
www.cafemila.co.uk

'We wanted to find somewhere to have a quick coffee and cake stop whilst in Godalming. All of the other cafés seemed to be heaving so we found *Café Mila* just off the High Street which was quieter. They had a really good range of cakes on offer – the chocolate cake was amazing!! We got our son a Smarties cookie which he loved. It was surprisingly child-friendly for a small café – highchairs available (the Ikea brand ones) and lots of things for children to eat (smaller portions of the adult menu). The food did look really good and very tempting – their signature dish is a falafel pitta which I am keen to try (maybe next time!). There were also plenty of soups, meze plates and salads on offer. Although we didn't use the baby change, I did take a peek and was pleasantly surprised to see a whole little changing area and also a step up to the sink for children – fantastic! There is space in the café for pushchairs – but not much! There are, however, tables outside with plenty of space for you to bring your pram to the table if the weather is good. A lovely café which we would definitely recommend.'
Victoria, mum to Freddy

'Although this isn't a huge place, there is a covered outdoors space and an upstairs area too and we have always left the buggy outside with no worries. They have a baby change area although it's separate from the toilet and they have a cosy corner perfect for breastfeeding, while the bucket of toys keeps toddlers amused. The food is excellent, homemade, big servings and very reasonably priced. They do a wide range of drinks and are always thinking of new and interesting options such as their fruit and vegetable juices which taste so much better than they sound. The staff are really friendly and lovely towards babies.'
Claire, mum to Orson

Costa
www.costa.co.uk
Guildford Spectrum, Parkway, GU1 1UP

'*Costa* at *Spectrum* (see page 60) has good highchairs for feeding.'
Cat, mum to Poppy

'This is a great place to pop into to put back on all the calories burnt off in one of the various toddler swimming sessions (see pages 6, 60 and 90). They do the usual *Costa* fare and the juices and smoothies are always a big hit with Daniel meaning I get to enjoy a drink of my own!'
Gemma, mum to Daniel

Guildford Children's Centre

Hazel Avenue, Bellfields, GU1 1NR
01483 566589
www.guildfordchildrenscentre.surrey.sch.uk
(Also see *Guildford Children's Centre on* pages 93 and 162)

'Hazel Avenue *Children's Centre* has a little café with good value food and tasty cakes. There are toys for small children and plenty of other parents to meet so it's easy to go alone. They also have an outdoor area which is a real suntrap although there's enough shade to take babies.'
Claire, mum to Orson

Mummas and Beans

10 Queen Street, Godalming, GU7 1BD
01483 808842
www.mummasandbeans.co.uk
(Also see *Mummas and Beans* on page 62)

'Baby-friendly café offering drinks and scrummy cakes with a small sandwich selection. Fairly small but room for buggies with about six tables. Baby food for sale and use of cups, highchairs etc. for babies. Various classes take place and there is a playroom open at certain times along with crèche facilities. A beauty room is available offering various treatments and baby can sit in playpen to watch. Breastfeeding friendly.'
Cat, mum to William

'*Mummas and Beans* is a great place designed for parents/carers and children. They have a café at the front and a playroom at the back that serves as a crèche and also a studio for classes.'
Claire, mum to Orson

Pinnock's Coffee House

High Street, Ripley, GU23 6AF
01483 222419
www.pinnockscoffeehouse.com

'*Pinnock's Coffee House* has only been open since July 2012, but it's already got a good following and I am a complete convert after a recent visit. When I stepped into this beautiful 15th century building, the guy behind the counter leapt out to give me a hand with my pram, and when I asked where I could breastfeed, said that anywhere was fine but if I wanted to be really comfy, I could go upstairs. So after I'd placed my

order (no mean feat with a choice of three hot chocolates – dark, milk and white, and all made with real chocolate – drip coffee and a mouthwatering display of cakes and slices), I was given another lift upstairs with my pram and entered my absolute paradise! From now on, this is my favourite place to feed ... myself and Alexander. While I sipped on my delicious dark hot chocolate and sat in one of the gorgeous squashy armchairs, I read one of the books from their extensive swapping-library. Very happy! Downstairs is kitted out in more of a café style, while upstairs makes the most of the oak beams and wooden floors, with a really cosy atmosphere and a whole wall full of books. There will be plenty of space for our entire NCT group when I drag them along next week. Next time I'll probably leave the pram downstairs or in the car, but I really hope this new establishment is appreciated as it should be. Don't miss the baby change – it can't be adequately described, you'll just have to visit.'
Suzie, mum to Alexander

RHS Garden Wisley
Woking, GU23 6QB
0845 260 9000
www.rhs.org.uk/Gardens/Wisley
(Also see *RHS Garden Wisley* on page 34)

CAFÉS AND BARS

'*RHS Garden Wisley* has two restaurants, two cafés and a coffee shop. They serve a good range of hot and cold food and have some of the best cakes around. They bake their own bread and produce their own fruit and vegetables, all of which are served onsite. There are basic baby changing facilities although I usually just change Ethan out in the spacious gardens. One of the cafés has a soft play area for children up to five years old and they do have an area for nursing mums although it's just a couple of tables.'
Cath, mum to Ethan

Starbucks
Sainsbury's, Bowers Farm Lane, Burpham, GU4 7JU
01483 301082
www.starbucks.co.uk

'We love stopping off here for a drink and snack. Quiet enough during the day for breastfeeding and plenty of highchairs available for toddlers. The staff make the best babycinnos for little toddlers who can't drink out of an open cup yet (use the spoon to eat the froth). People-watching galore!'
Vicky, mum to Amelia

Surrey Sports Park, University of Surrey, Richard Meyjes Road, GU2 7AD (for sat nav use GU2 7XX)
01483 689111
www.surreysportspark.co.uk/Starbucks

'*Starbucks* is a great place to enjoy a cuppa, cake or snack with a friend or group of friends and as it's a larger space than you'd usually get in most other coffee shops, it's quite buggy-friendly. There's a lift to take you to the floor it's on, and you don't even have to be a member at the *Sports Park* to visit!
It's situated within the *Surrey Sports Park* (see page 61) in Guildford which is just off the A3, near the Royal Surrey Hospital and not too far from Guildford mainline station and town centre. Open every day from around 7am until late, with lots of free car parking, there's plenty of indoor seating which overlooks the sports halls, as well as a sun terrace with outdoor seats and views over the pitches where you can watch any sports going on.
Free Wi-fi internet access is also available, you just need to ask a member of staff for an access code. Baby change facilities are available at the centre and I've always used the one just down the corridor from the coffee shop, which has been clean, functional and of adequate size. It's also opposite the viewing gallery overlooking the pool, so we stop and watch the swimming for a bit which my son Charlie always loves!'
Carolyn, mum to Charlie

CAFÉS AND BARS

Tillings Café
55 Station Road, Gomshall, GU5 9NP
01483 202 214
www.tillingscafe.co.uk

'*Tillings* is a spacious café with really friendly staff and they do amazing homemade cakes, some of which are gluten free. There's lots of parking and they have clean baby change facilities. I really recommend it as a great place to relax with friends and treat yourself. There are good walks nearby too.'
Miriam, mum to Abigail

'*Tillings* in Gomshall is a large quirky building with a café downstairs. They have a large car park at the back and amazing homemade cakes for a real treat.'
Claire, mum to Orson

15. Restaurants and Pubs
Susan Sanderson, mum to Thomas and Harry

It really is amazing how your priorities change once you have kids. Before we joined the parenthood club there was nothing my husband and I loved more than going out on a Friday (and, gasp, even a Saturday!) night for fantastic food and drink. The only worries I would have were which cuisine to try tonight and do they have a happy hour? While we're fortunate that we can occasionally still get to enjoy a much cherished 'date night' thanks to lovely friends and family offering to babysit, most of the time our eating out now takes place in daylight and involves having two small boys in tow. Our priorities have changed somewhat and now focus on 'do they do a kids' menu?', 'are there highchairs available?' and 'do they get free crayons?' – times have certainly changed! Over the last three years we thought we'd probably tried most of the family-friendly pubs and restaurants in and around Guildford but there really are some new gems in this chapter – I can't wait to try them with my family and hope you will too – happy eating!

Guildford Town Centre

Côte
35 Castle Street, GU1 3UQ
01483 579714
www.cote-restaurants.co.uk

'*Côte Bistro* is a lovely place to eat when you're in town. The last time we were there, they really couldn't do enough to help, from adjusting the air con so it was right on us, to helping move the buggies into an out of the way space – they were just great.'
Cath, mum to Ethan

RESTAURANTS AND PUBS

Giraffe
215-217 High Street, GU1 3BJ
01483 300237
www.giraffe.net

'*Giraffe* is a well-known haunt for new mums meeting up with babies. Every time I have been there, especially during the day, there have been many parents and children. We used to meet here regularly with my NCT group. The restaurant has a good noisy atmosphere so you don't feel like you have to be quiet if your baby is screaming the place down! The menu is quite varied and is a mixture of american/thai/healthy options etc. You can also just have a coffee there. Plenty of highchairs (and I mean plenty – we once turned up with eight babies in highchairs and they didn't bat an eyelid!!). Seriously, the staff here are really used to babies/children. The changing area is spacious and clean – situated at the back of the restaurant. They also provide crayons etc. for the children and will warm bottles etc. The restaurant is quite large but if busy then you may need to leave your pram at the entrance – if not then you can easily wheel it in to your table.'
Victoria, mum to Freddy

Jamie's Italian
13 Friary Street, GU1 4EH
01483 600920
www.jamieoliver.com/italian/guildford

'I was a bit worried when we first went to *Jamie's* with our baby as it is often busy and I was concerned there wouldn't be space for our pram – baby was too young to sit in a highchair. But the staff couldn't have been more helpful, moving tables around for us so that there was space for his pram next to us, and with so many other children in at lunchtime, I wasn't worried at all about him waking up. In the end, however, he slept all the way through lunch thanks to the low level background noise. We will definitely be going to *Jamie's* again!'
Suzie, mum to Alexander

'Very popular Italian restaurant. Often has a 'kids eat free' offer on during the week which is the time to go as otherwise quite expensive and portions not big enough to share! Kids' menu comes on a cool viewer – great for older children (four years plus). They usually provide colouring sheets and pencils and unlimited cordial with meals. Can get very hectic, noisy and crowded and often has a queue at weekends but not too bad during the week. Buggies cannot be taken to the table but they will store for you and bring back at the end of the meal. Baby changing is downstairs but upstairs is quieter and less hot (away from kitchen) and if you can get a window

booth, children can watch all the buses go past!'
Kath, mum to Callum and Lucas

The Keystone
3 Portsmouth Road, GU2 4BL
01483 575089
www.thekeystone.co.uk

'*The Keystone* was one of our favourite pre-baby pubs in Guildford, with a varied menu of homemade and often seasonal food including some good veggie options, a friendly community vibe, and some interesting events (for example, Café Scientifique, a monthly opportunity to discuss current issues in science – a bit different to an average night out in the pub).
It's remained a favourite since our little one was born, particularly for lunch. I've found it to be a friendly place, with no problems breastfeeding. They're currently running a Sunday Funday: under-tens eat free (one child per paying adult), plus there's fancy dress, board games and chalkboards for doodling. Main courses are mostly between £7-10, with the kids' menu £4-5. If your little one has particular food requirements, or is just a bit fussy, their chef should be able to accommodate you even if what's on the menu isn't quite right (we experienced this with a friend with multiple allergies with no problems). One downside is that there are no baby changing facilities. It's quite quiet in the afternoons, and could be a good place to meet up with friends. They also have a reservable area with sofas for events and get-togethers.'
Bronwen, mum to Olwen

Loch Fyne
Centenary Hall, Chapel Street, GU1 3UH
01483 230550
www.lochfyne-restaurants.com/restaurants/Guildford

'*Loch Fyne* is a decent restaurant that makes a real effort for children. The children's menu (and the adult's for that matter) is excellent, the service equally good and generally supported by the staff making a real effort towards the children. Not a location you would necessarily expect to go with toddlers but one well worth trying if you fancy something different. The only real drawback is the access arrangements – the restaurant is on the first floor (and the toilets on the second) with pushchairs needing to be left on the lower ground floor. However, the staff have always been happy to assist with moving pushchairs and the added entertainment that comes from being able to show children the fish, lobsters etc. on ice at the counter more than make up for the slight access challenges.'
Peter, dad to Thomas and Oliver

RESTAURANTS AND PUBS

Nando's
11-12 Friary Street, GU1 4EH
01483 568083
www.nandos.co.uk

'The great thing about *Nando's* is that the food doesn't take very long to arrive. It is child-friendly with highchairs, baby changing, a children's menu and activity packs.'
Gemma, mum to Daniel

Pizza Express
237-241 High Street, GU1 3BJ
01483 300122
www.pizzaexpress.com/visit-a-restaurant/restaurant/guildford

'I have found the staff at *Pizza Express* often go out of their way to help me when I go in alone with the boys: opening doors, bringing balloons and even pre-cutting my pizza into little squares to help me eat with one hand while feeding or jiggling a baby on one knee. Every little definitely helps!'
Amy, mum to Thomas and Oliver

'If all else fails – go to *Pizza Express*! Yes, you've probably been loads of times before but the food is good and there is always something healthy on the menu for your little one. The Guildford branch is very spacious and there are always plenty of highchairs available. It's quite a lively atmosphere so you never need to worry if your child is having a loud day! I often see many new mothers breastfeeding in there and the staff are very relaxed about it. There is plenty of room for prams to be left at the entrance to the restaurant or even by your table if it's not too busy. Food is consistently good – you can normally get vouchers for two for one deals online as well if you have a look. (They do a deal menu on a Friday night too – just in case you're after a cheap night out without the kids!).'
Victoria, mum to Freddy

The Stoke Pub and Pizzeria
103 Stoke Road, GU1 4JN
01483 504296
www.thestoke.co.uk

'Manager is child-friendly and there are lots of toys available to be used. Pizzas are fantastic and made fresh so good for kids. Baby change facilities available. Decor is a little dark though, but otherwise a reasonable choice for lunch particularly!'
Cathy, mum to Alex

TGI Friday's

2 North Street, GU1 4AA
0844 692 0271
www.tgifridays.co.uk/guildford

'We had lunch here on my son's second birthday and thought it was great for little ones. Daniel was given an activity pack when we got there and there is a separate children's menu. They noticed it was his birthday and gave him a balloon and put candles in the dessert so we could sing 'Happy Birthday' to him. So definitely on my list of places to go back to!'
Gemma, mum to Daniel

Wagamama

25-29 High Street, GU1 3DY
01483 457779
www.wagamama.com

'Good for (and with) spawn.'
Chris, dad to Daniel

'My friends have children who will happily graze through the whole menu at *Wagamama*, ours are more limited (chicken katsu – hold the curry sauce) but the staff are friendly and don't seem to worry too much about how much ends up on the floor. For me, however, the best thing about this place is that when you have managed to round up a babysitter and are desperate to get out but truly would rather be in bed, you can come here, talk to a grown-up, share some nourishing food and a cheeky beer or saintly juice and still be in bed by half nine. Bliss.'
Katie, mum to Beth and Asa

Out of Town

The Abinger Hatch

Abinger Lane, Abinger Common, Near Dorking, RH5 6HZ
01306 730737
www.theabingerhatch.com

'*The Abinger Hatch* is a country pub with great food and a large garden in a lovely quiet rural setting in Abinger Common. The food is averagely priced and it has a good beer selection too. It has a church and graveyard opposite for exploring with the kids, a playground just next to it, and there are local walks you can do as well.

It can be busy on Sundays and it is advisable to book a table if there are more than four of you. All this makes it a really lovely Sunday afternoon out. It is close to local villages on the A25 Dorking Road if you want to go to Gomshall and *Shere* (see page 45) as well.'
Chris, dad to Eliza and Wilfred

The Anchor
Pyrford Lock, Wisley, GU23 6QW
01932 342507
www.anchorpyrford.co.uk

'Lovely sunshine/outside location, plenty of indoor and outdoor seating by the canal. Great walk along the canal/feed ducks. Just for coffee/drinks or a meal. Great baby change, plenty of parking.'
Cat, mum to William

The Black Swan
Old Lane, Ockham, KT11 1NG
01932 862364
www.blackswanockham.com

'Good outdoor play area with children's games and plenty of space to run about. Indoors is also spacious, with open fires and comfy seating. They have a kids' menu as well as really great food in general (a barbecue on one of our visits) and guest beers and ciders. Not the cheapest food, but good quality. The car park is big although gravel, so not the easiest with a pram. My main reason for recommending this pub, however, is that they have a large baby change facility, well-stocked with a variety of free nappies and wipes, which is really appreciated.'
Tony, dad to Alexander

The Cricketers
Downside Common, Downside, Cobham, KT11 3NX
01932 862105
www.thecricketersdownside.co.uk

'Lovely old village pub near Cobham, situated adjacent to Downside common. A recent change of ownership has meant a welcome revamp of the interior and menu. The menu now has a strongly Italian slant, with some contemporary classics and sharing platters. The main selling point though has to be the fabulous child-friendly location – a large terrace leads onto the common with its wide expanse of grass and two separate play areas – something for everyone. A great spot to while

away a Sunday afternoon – bring a rug.'
Ruth, mum to George and William

IKEA

West Quay Road, Southampton, Hampshire, SO15 1GY
0845 225 7125
www.ikea.com/gb/en/store/southampton

'If you happen to be in Southampton or *IKEA*, definitely visit the restaurant to get your lunch. They do great lunch boxes for little ones. Not only are they cheap (about £2) but unlike many child lunch boxes, the contents of these are all organic and healthy and toddler appropriate. Of course they also provide plenty of highchairs and the adult meals are quite nice too.'
Vicky, mum to Amelia

The Inn on the Lake

Ockford Road, Godalming, GU7 1RH
01483 419997
www.theinnonthelake.co.uk

'*The Inn on the Lake* pub is an excellent venue for families in the summer months as it has a large garden which the children can run around in (and babies can happily coo in their prams) and there are always plenty of free tables. The food and drinks are very good but very much gastro pub prices so be prepared to spend a fair bit! The menu caters for a variety of tastes and there is a good selection of both alcoholic and non-alcoholic beverages.
The baby change facilities are located in the disabled toilet which means they are not always available when you have a baby that desperately needs changing! Having said that, you could always find a quiet spot on the grass if it's a nice day!
The pub is situated on a steep hill but you need not worry as there is a ramp at the front suitable for buggies and a pathway for the garden area. This pub does have a really friendly and relaxed atmosphere and we have enjoyed many happy times there both pre and post baby so I would definitely recommend it!'
Abi, mum to Oliver

The Jovial Sailor

Portsmouth Road, Ripley, GU23 6EZ
01483 342605
www.chefandbrewer.com/pub/jovial-sailor-ripley-woking/c0443

'*The Jovial Sailor* is a large pub with lots of parking, plenty of space for pushchairs,

and they offer baby change and highchairs as well as a good menu, flexible food for children and a beer garden. We went there with some NCT friends and found they had everything we needed for a relaxing evening out, and we didn't feel we were in the way as we sometimes feel with crying babies. The staff were helpful and friendly and we'll enjoy going here again.'
Tony, dad to Alexander

The Mill at Elstead
Farnham Road, Elstead, GU8 6LE
01252 703333
www.millelstead.co.uk

'I have been taking our son, Sam, to *The Mill* regularly since he was about five weeks old. It is a very convenient place for us to meet my husband for Friday lunch as it is close to his work. They are very child-friendly and will gladly help you up the stairs with the pushchair or carry your drink to the table if you have your hands full. They have baby changing facilities which are clean and convenient to use. They serve good pub food, and although a little more expensive than other pubs, the beautiful gardens and the river full of ducks makes for very pleasant and picturesque surroundings on a summer's day. Great if you have children who love feeding ducks!'
Nicky, mum to Sam

The Onslow Arms
The Street, West Clandon, GU4 7TE
01483 222447
www.onslowarmsclandon.co.uk

'*The Onslow Arms* is a super country 'gastro style' pub which has very recently been fully refurbished. It's approximately 15 minutes by car from central Guildford. They are baby and toddler friendly offering highchairs and a good children's menu – the Sunday menu also offers child portions of main meals. The baby changing facilities are great; a separate room (located next to the ladies' toilets) which is decorated with nursery style wallpaper and even has a shelf of cuddly toys!
The feature we especially like about the *Onslow Arms* is the outside area – there is a large walled patio with some good shady spots and some more secluded garden seating. Parking is plentiful and there is also a helipad – we have seen helicopters landing on two occasions!! Lastly, located on the common opposite the pub is a lovely children's playground (see *West Clandon Playground* on page 51) catering for toddlers up to teenagers.
Note: The playground does not belong to the pub and is across the busy main road.'
Zoe, mum to Imogen

RESTAURANTS AND PUBS

The Parrot
Forest Green, RH5 5RZ
01306 621339
www.theparrot.co.uk

'Well worth the drive, this gloriously rustic pub has a reassuringly short menu, many of the dishes on which are made with meat from the pub's own farm. I nearly always have the rib-eye and have never yet been disappointed. Not outrageously child-friendly, but they have always tolerated ours, which is high praise. There is also a great farm shop/deli with a fabulous cheese room.'
Katie, mum to Beth and Asa

The Parrot Inn
Broadford Road, Shalford, GU4 8DW
01483 561400
www.parrotinn.co.uk

'We have been here a few times for Sunday lunch with our baby. They are happy to provide highchairs and if you let them know you have children, they tend to place you with other families so that you feel more comfortable if your little one makes a noise. The Sunday roasts are excellent so you do need to book in advance to ensure that you get a table. A great location for a walk along the river afterwards.'
Nicky, mum to Sam

Prezzo
8 Queen Street, Godalming, GU7 1BD
01483 428746
www.prezzorestaurants.co.uk/restaurant/godalming

'Large open plan restaurant with lovely high ceilings. All on one level – use furthest door if you have a buggy. Can get quite noisy but great if you have children as you don't feel like you are disturbing other people too much! Ask for one of the big round tables or a booth for a bit more privacy. Highchairs are available and they have friendly waiting staff. There's also baby changing.
There's an open pizza oven so children can see pizzas being made and cooked – and they often get a free chef's hat into the bargain!
Kids' menu is less than £6 (at last visit) which includes three courses and the portions are plenty to share between two younger children (five years) if you want or they will pack up any leftovers to take home. Kids' menu comes with a sheet of stickers and puzzles and they usually have colouring pencils too if you ask.'
Kath, mum to Callum and Lucas

RESTAURANTS AND PUBS

The Row Barge
Riverside, GU1 1LW
01483 573358
www.rowbargeguildford.com

'Situated on the riverside just off Stoughton Road, *The Row Barge* is a great little hidden gem. The waterside garden is beautiful in the summer, with lots of boats to watch going past, although you'll need to keep beady eyes on adventurous toddlers as there is no barrier to the water. During the day it's child-friendly, although not very well geared-up, so take your changing mat and a pop-up highchair.
Food during the week is proper, old-fashioned pub grub (sausages, ham egg and chips etc.), but well cooked and with good quality meats sourced from local farms and butchers. On Sundays it's roast dinner only, but with a choice of four. There is a weekday/Saturday children's menu, and small portions of roast on Sundays.
For mums and dads this is 2012's CAMRA Surrey pub of the year, with great guest real ales, good west country ciders and a reasonable selection of wines.'
Katie, mum to Sebastian and Alexander

The Royal Anchor
9-11 The Square, Liphook, Hampshire, GU30 7AD
01428 722244
www.royalanchor-liphook.co.uk

'We stopped here on a wet summer's day hoping they would feed four hungry adults, two energetic children and two grizzly babies at 3pm. Not only do they serve food all day but they offer a lot more. As you enter there's a brightly lit cake display to ensure you can't get away without the kids all having a piece. Watch out though, these slices were too much for all of us put together and we only ordered two! We found plenty of space to sit down with buggies next to us and clean, sturdy highchairs too. In fact if we'd got there earlier we could have grabbed one of the booths with a TV screen showing CBeebies!
The menu has a huge range of basic pub grub for very reasonable prices. They also have a separate children's and even a babies' menu. They seem to do different deals each day and we turned up on a Tuesday which was kids' meals for £1 day – hurrah, no worries if they leave some. The food came quickly and afterwards the kids went outside to play on the playground. If it had been nicer we could have used the large garden which had plenty more space for big groups of noisy children.
It is part of the Hungry Horse chain which I've not been to before so all this may be standard if you have one near you, but we were very pleased with our find!'
Claire, mum to Orson

RESTAURANTS AND PUBS

The Seahorse
The Street, Shalford, GU4 8BU
01483 514351
www.theseahorseguildford.co.uk

'This is a nice pub, with a great choice of food, tolerant staff and some interesting drinks. The garden is pretty child-friendly and there are plenty of places inside to pop a sleeping baby in a car seat while you enjoy eating with two hands! Parking can be tricky on busy days.'
Katie, mum to Beth and Asa

The Slug and Lettuce
54/56 High Street, Godalming, GU7 1DY
01483 527134
www.slugandlettuce.co.uk/godalming

'50% off all food on Mondays including Bank Holidays – a great day to go for a bargain but get there early as service can sometimes be a bit slow as it gets very busy. Children's menu ok (pasta etc.) – comes with a small dish of cucumber and carrots and a sheet of puzzles and stickers – price includes a drink (although usually a Capri Sun!) and ice cream. Selection of toys and lots of highchairs and children's cutlery. Baby changing downstairs, main toilet upstairs.'
Kath, mum to Callum and Lucas

The Squirrel Inn
Hurtmore Road, Hurtmore, GU7 2RN
01483 860223
www.thesquirrel-hurtmore.co.uk

'Located just off the A3 in the village of Hurtmore, near Godalming and Guildford, *The Squirrel* is a friendly pub with a cosy traditional feel, also offering a large restaurant area, ample parking and plenty of covered and uncovered outdoor seating areas for those wonderful summer days and evenings we get!! As well as themed food evenings, locally sourced food and a good selection of real ales from across the country, they do a great Sunday roast lunch and we often go there now with our four month old son Charlie, where we've found the staff to be friendly, helpful and more than happy to accommodate babies/small children/families. They offer highchairs, have a children's menu and a child-friendly garden play area. Baby change facilities are located in the foyer of the ladies toilets. Online booking can be made through their website. Good food, good value and good atmosphere.'
Carolyn, mum to Charlie

The White Hart
The Green, Pirbright, Woking, GU24 0LP
01483 799715
www.thewhitehartpirbright.co.uk

'Great food and very willing to help with little ones. There are spacious toilets for changing and a good children's menu. We have been a couple of times with a large group of friends and they coped very well. There is a large green opposite which is great for running off a bit of steam or taking a quick break between courses.'
Carla, mum to Ellis

The White Horse
The Street, Hascombe, Godalming, GU8 4JA
01483 208258
www.whitehorsehascombe.co.uk

'Lovely country pub and fairly child-friendly. Only two booster seats (no highchairs) so worth asking when you book or taking your own. No baby changing facilities so be prepared to use back of your car or toilet floor. Children's menu available or they will do children's portions of main meals.
Big shady garden with pub bench style tables and a few more 'formal' tables with parasols if you want to eat outside and keep an eye on children. Inside there is a selection of children's toys and books – some with missing pieces but never seems to bother children. Friendly staff (and a couple of friendly pub dogs).
A good choice for Saturday or Sunday lunch after a walk at *Winkworth Arboretum* (see page 32) – in winter they have a wood burning stove and in summer you can sit in the garden.'
Kath, mum to Callum and Lucas

Worplesdon Place Hotel
Perry Hill, Worplesdon, GU3 3RY
01483 232407
www.worplesdonplace.com

'From the outside, this doesn't look like a very exciting venue ... another Beefeater and Premier Inn that looks like all the others. But for parents with young children, this is worth a visit on a nice day, for the outside space alone. The indoors pub area is spacious, clean and child-friendly, with baby change facilities, and the outdoors has a huge beer garden with plenty of tables, lots of grass and space to run around in, and a lake with its own resident ducks.'

Tony, dad to Alexander

The Wotton Hatch
Guildford Road, Wotton, Dorking, RH5 6QQ
01306 887694
www.wottonhatch.co.uk

'A really lovely pub with a great garden and splendid food, it's ideal with the kids in the summer and a cosy place for a grown-up evening out in the winter.'
Katie, mum to Beth and Asa

16. Public Transport
Carla Applegate, mum to Ellis

Going on public transport with your little one needn't be a terrible hassle. Going prepared is almost essential and, although Guildford might not have the best public transport in the world, most places are accessible one way or another. For little ones, it's all part of the adventure! We hope this information will help ease the journey. So, take some tips from below and see if public transport can help expand your horizons.

'I don't drive, so all excursions with the little one are either on foot or by bus or train. I've found it easier than I expected, so here are my top tips for using public transport with a baby:

- Look up train and bus times ahead of time – I use *www.nationalrail.co.uk* for trains and *www.traveline.info* for buses. Make sure to look up your return journey too (I used to be the sort of person who just figured this out on the way home but you don't want to get stuck with a long wait with baby in tow!).
- Be on (or ahead of) time! Better to be five minutes early than miss your train and end up having to entertain baby for half an hour.
- Ask for help if you need it. You'll probably find people will offer to help with things like getting the buggy on the train, or to lend a hand with bags, but if they don't, just ask!
- I find using a sling easier than taking a buggy, but have done both. With a buggy, look out for wheelchair or bike spaces on the train (wheelchair spaces are normally better as you should be able to sit next to the buggy).
- Be adventurous. I was inspired by a friend of mine who took his baby daughter to visit friends in Italy on his own, so I decided to travel to Derby to see an old friend. Despite picking one of the few hot days we had this summer, the trip went really well and it was lovely to catch up with her

155

and her family.

Having a baby and no car needn't stop you getting out and having fun!'

Bronwen, mum to Olwen

'Relying on public transport can be challenging when you have a little one. Buses in central Guildford are often late on peak hours and early on off-peak hours; trains, in my experience, are more reliable, but they are also subject to unforeseen circumstances such as accidents, weather conditions, a conductor who hasn't arrived, etc. However, there are positive aspects, too: you can give your full attention to your child and have a good time together singing, reading or talking about what you see with no other worries; if your child happens to nap during the journey, you can treat yourself to some 'me-time'. It teaches your child patience and it keeps you smart and alert to deal with those 'unforeseen circumstances' (of which parenthood is full!); it offers you various opportunities to teach your child cordiality and awareness of strangers.

Here is a personal short list of 'must-haves':

- water, a not-too-messy snack and a book;
- for journeys longer than an hour, I also take a travel scribbler or a children's magazine with stickers and other drawing/colouring activities;
- your personal memorised library of songs and rhymes – especially those which allow you to create new verses when the bus is running 20 minutes late (or more!), like the famous 'the wheels on the...';
- the phone number for a local cab company;
- readiness to fold your pushchair in case there is no space for you in the buggy bay, or there is no buggy bay.

I found a backpack carrier of inestimable value for train journeys, as many train stations don't have step-free access to all platforms. Also, stations can be very busy and you don't want your little one running around on a platform! During shorter journeys, I sometimes keep my daughter in the backpack throughout the journey and 'sit' the backpack next to me, so that I can keep hold of it. She can have a better view through the window and she is less likely to be tempted to run around inside the train.

We also have a 'travel routine' for journeys which we do regularly. I have a few familiar points which help create a sort of 'travel routine': the same games to and from the bus stop, same key words for crossing the road, finding a seat in the bus or pressing the stop button (a real must with my daughter). Counting pebbles or flowers, for example, is a good way to slow down or speed up your walk to the bus stop!

Finally, endless patience, creativity and a sense of humour are all helpful – but, being a parent, that is to be expected!'

Renata, mum to Winnie

PUBLIC TRANSPORT

'Getting the train and onto a London bus with a buggy wasn't the headache I had thought it might be. It would be easier with the carrier, but I usually have far too much to carry! I had to lift the buggy up the rather high gap onto the train, but there are lots of people to offer help, and the guard is always on the platform if you don't want to rely on strangers. Getting on and off the bus was easier although my chunky buggy doesn't quite fit down the aisle, but a little manoeuvering and all is fine! Do be prepared to fold up or wait for another bus if a wheelchair user needs the space, but generally it's no problem. I always avoid travelling at peak times if I possibly can so that there is plenty of space.'
Carla, mum to Ellis

Some helpful numbers and websites:

National Rail	08457 48 49 50	*www.nationalrail.co.uk*
Traveline	0871 200 2233	*www.traveline.org.uk*
		www.travelinesoutheast.org.uk
Transport for London	0843 222 1234	*www.tfl.gov.uk*

Some of the easiest places to reach by public transport:

By bus

Clandon Park
(See pages 30 and 58)
From Guildford bus station, take the number 463 (Arriva) bus.

Claremont Landscape Garden
(See page 30)
Take the 515 (Abellio Surrey) from Guildford bus station. If you show your bus tickets at the entrance, you will be given money off vouchers for the café.

Guildford Spectrum
(See pages 60,67, 90 and 109)
The number 100 bus runs from Guildford bus station.

RHS Garden Wisley
(See page 34)
Bus 515 (Abellio Surrey) from Guildford bus station.

PUBLIC TRANSPORT

Rokers Little Angels
(See pages 66 and 112)
From Guildford bus station, take the number 20 (Stagecoach).

By train:

Kew Gardens
(See page 33)
Take the train to Clapham Junction then change for Kew Bridge.

London: South Bank etc.
(See page 45)
Just a short walk from Waterloo, or check the bus routes and travel a bit further afield!

Watercress Line
(See page 22)
Take the train to Aldershot then change onto the Alton service.

17. Services
Gemma Gregson, mum to Daniel

Having a baby opens up a whole new world of issues to deal with. Perhaps you have decided you want to use washable nappies but don't know where to start, or you have a baby with feeding problems that you need to find a solution to. Maybe you just want to find out what's on in the area, or where to go for information and support on a particular topic. This chapter includes information on a wide range of services offered locally and we hope you find it helpful.

Breastfeeding Services

Breastfeeding can be a very rewarding experience for both mother and baby but the breastfeeding road is not always a smooth one. Fortunately, help is at hand with a range of breastfeeding services offering information and support at whatever stage your little one is at. A quick internet search will give you a list of lots of organisations and the NCT can also help. Further information on the NCT's breastfeeding services can be found on page 10 in the *All About the NCT* chapter.

Breastfeeding Cafés
Gomshall Mill, Gomshall, GU5 9LB
Guildford Children's Centre, Hazel Avenue, Bellfields, GU1 1NR
Mummas and Beans, 10 Queen Street, Godalming, GU7 1BD
07833 902 229 (Ruth Fromow)
www.bestfeeding.org.uk

'There's a feeding café with a lactation consultant called Ruth who moves between Gomshall Mill, Hazel Avenue *Children's Centre* and *Mummas and Beans*. It costs £2 which includes a drink and Ruth is just brilliant. She was a midwife but retrained in lactation and seems to know everything about everything. It's a great place to learn about weaning as well as breastfeeding and is a chance to chat to other new mums.'
Amelia, mum to Ivy

Guildford Drop-in Breastfeeding Clinics

The Spinney, Guildford Grove Children's Centre, Southway, GU2 8YD

Level B, Antenatal Clinic, Parentcraft room, Royal Surrey County Hospital, GU2 7XX

www.royalsurrey.nhs.uk/Maternity/Feeding-Your-Baby

'We attended the feeding clinic a couple of times and they were great with very practical and sympathetic advice. Our son had a small tongue tie and didn't quite put on enough weight in his first weeks. Ruth is incredibly experienced and a quick nip and we were done. After that they helped with breastfeeding advice and ensuring he continued to do well.'

Carla, mum to Ellis

'The clinic at the hospital was fantastic. Alexander was a fair feeder from the outset, but at around ten days/two weeks, we found that he wasn't putting weight on as quickly as expected, and I was in a lot of pain. The friendly staff at the drop-in helped me with his positioning and answered my questions about timings, duration and so on, and really turned things around for us. He started putting weight on immediately and I was much more comfortable.'

Suzie, mum to Alexander

Children's Centres

Sure Start *Children's Centres* provide support and information to parents and carers. Each centre tends to be different as what's on offer is tailored to meet the needs of the local community. The ones in Guildford offer a whole of host of services including breastfeeding support, weaning workshops, child health clinics, various drop-in sessions for parents and little ones to play together, exercise classes, childcare, and also adult courses in subjects such as IT, Maths and English. Activities can vary each term so it's worth having a look at the websites or popping in to pick up a leaflet. They are great places to meet other parents and carers and can provide useful support as you journey through parenthood.

'Sure Start *Children's Centres* are a brilliant place to find out what's going on and meet other parents and carers. They have a range of activities such as *Play and Learn* sessions (see page 104), baby massage and new parent courses and baby clinics where you can get your baby weighed and talk to a health professional. They run regular weaning workshops and also a course of yoga based story sessions. They also have notice boards where other activities are advertised and they stock parenting magazines such as Family Grapevine and leaflets for local organisations. The staff are really helpful and friendly and the breastfeeding clinic has been helping mums get through difficult times with great success.'

Claire, mum to Orson

SERVICES

Boxgrove Children's Centre
Boxgrove Primary School, Boxgrove Lane, Merrow, GU1 2TD
01483 540818
bcc@boxgrove.surrey.sch.uk
www.boxgrovechildrenscentre.co.uk

'A small Sure Start Centre at Boxgrove School which runs a postnatal baby massage and yoga class, new mums' group for babies up to six months (Hatchlings), another group for babies up to ten months (Owlets) and finally another one for babies up to 18 months (Fledglings). Also a swimming class and various other *Play and Learn* options with special events during school holidays. The staff are really friendly and supportive, allowing members to share experiences and offer age-appropriate advice.'
Vicky, mum to Amelia

Guildford Children's Centre
Hazel Avenue, Bellfields, GU1 1NR
01483 566589
admin@guildfordchildrenscentre.surrey.sch.uk
www.guildfordchildrenscentre.surrey.sch.uk

Town Centre Site, York Road, GU1 4DU
01483 561652
info@guildfordchildrenscentre.surrey.sch.uk
www.guildfordchildrenscentre.surrey.sch.uk

'The Bellfields *Children's Centre* offers loads of activities including a buggy walk which is great for meeting people and having a look around the local area, a music class for babies under three and a keep fit class. They also run parenting courses, hold introduction to weaning sessions as well as the *Play and Learn* groups (see page 104) each week. There is a crèche and also a café (see page 137) where you can have lunch or coffee and a cake with all the new friends you meet at the centre. We like the staff and the fact that most of what they offer is free. Guildford has several centres so look up the one near you or drop into whichever has a class you fancy.'
Claire, mum to Orson

'The Bellfields *Children's Centre* is a fantastic facility for all families with young children from newborn up to school age. I have been taking my daughter regularly since she was just a few weeks old and am still taking her now at three.
The brilliant play sessions are divided into Fun on the Floor for babies not yet crawling, Babies on the Move for crawlers and wobbly walkers and then *Play and*

Learn (see page 104) for confident walkers. Younger ones love the fantastic sensory room with lights and sounds, while for older ones they have a seemingly endless stream of creative ideas using water/sand/mud/leaves/paint/play-doh/tactile foodstuffs. The outdoor area is great with a large green space for running about and a paved area for tricycles etc., there is also a large sandpit. This is by far my favourite of all of Guildford's large selection of playgroups (and I've tried them all!), and I think my daughter would agree – and there is the added bonus that these play sessions are free!

There is also a very good value café (see page 137) serving tasty homemade cakes and basic lunches, and the café has a gate to prevent toddlers from escaping, and plenty of toys and books to keep them entertained. They also have a drop-in clinic to get babies weighed/ask the health visitors questions about feeding/sleep issues etc., breastfeeding counselling sessions and music sessions called Movers and Shakers. They run all sorts of courses such as baby massage, weaning and parenting classes. There's even aerobics once a week with a free crèche. The centre is open all year round with special family fun days during school holidays.'

Jenny, mum to Abigail and Alistair

The Spinney, Guildford Grove Children's Centre
Southway, GU2 8YD
01483 510570
childrenscentre@guildfordgrove.surrey.sch.uk
www.thespinneycc.org.uk

'*The Spinney Children's Centre* is based at Guildford Grove Primary School in Park Barn. It's a convenient location with good parking (except at school-run time) and they run a range of facilities including antenatal and postnatal advice, breastfeeding support, *Play and Learn* (see page 105), baby massage, toy library and parenting courses. Staff are knowledgeable and friendly.'
Suzie, mum to Alexander

Children's Hairdressing

Getting your child's hair cut for the first time can be a big step for many parents. Unless you are brave enough to have a go with the scissors yourself, you will need to find somewhere that you, and more importantly your child, feel comfortable. Many hairdressing salons and barbers offer children's cuts so it's worth asking at your favourite hairdressers or why not try one of the following suggestions that have been 'tried and tested' by local children.

Close Shave
257 Merrow Heights, Epsom Road, GU1 2RE
01483 536444
www.closeshavebarbers.co.uk

'This friendly barbers in Merrow has a little red sports car for younger customers to sit in and keep busy while they receive a quick trim. If they sit quietly there might just be a lolly on offer at the end of the appointment.'
Katie, mum to Beth and Asa

Jacks of London
165 High Street, GU1 3AJ
01483 531406
www.jacksoflondon.com/guildford

'We have taken our little boy for a haircut twice at *Jacks* now and have been really pleased with the results. They give them a booster seat to sit on and the promise of a lollipop at the end kept Thomas in his seat long enough for a quick trim! Taking the iPad did help distract him as he wasn't too keen on the noise of the hairdryers!

Reasonably priced too at around £12 for a boy's cut.'
Susan, mum to Thomas and Harry

Spikes and Curls
61A Downing Street, Farnham, GU9 7PN
01252 711121
www.spikesandcurls-farnham.co.uk

'If, like mine, your kids are reluctant to have their hair cut, bring them to *Spikes and Curls* and you won't be able to drag them away!! Half toy shop, half hairdressers, children are lured into a fire-engine, racing car or other novelty chair, plied with raisins whilst they watch their favourite CBeebies TV show on their own telly. Now THAT'S how to do a haircut!! Both our boys had their first haircut here – and we came away with a certificate with a photo and a lock of hair – very sweet.'
Ruth, mum to George and William

Trotters
Unit 6, White Lion Walk, GU1 3DN
01483 454668
www.trotters.co.uk/t-store-Guildford.aspx
(Also see *Trotters* on page 124)

'With a fish tank and a selection of toys and books to distract the little ones when they are getting their hair cut this is a good place for first (and many more after that!) haircuts. We have been going regularly for about the last year or so and although Daniel doesn't like getting his hair cut, he tolerates it, which is helped by the fact that the staff are good with children and adept at doing super speedy haircuts. Of course, the promise of a chocolate coin from their stash helps too!'
Gemma, mum to Daniel

Cranial Osteopathy

Cranial osteopathy is a type of osteopathic treatment that seeks to encourage the release of stresses and strains throughout the body, including the head, and may help with a range of problems. For more information see *www.cranial.org.uk*

Donna Varns
Fairlands Avenue, Worplesdon, GU3 3NA
01483 594250
info@donnavarnsosteopathy.co.uk
www.donnavarnsosteopathy.co.uk

'*Donna Varns*, Cranial Osteopath is absolutely brilliant. She specialises in baby cranial osteopathy and is really understanding. She gave us great advice and transformed Caitlin who had problems with sleeping and feeding. In fact she gave me my life back.'
Miriam, mum to Caitlin

Laura Worsfold
The Holistic Centre, The Barn, Wiggins Yard, Bridge Street, Godalming, GU7 1HW
01483 418103
info@lwosteopath.co.uk
www.lwosteopath.co.uk

'*Laura Worsfold* is a cranial osteopath based in Godalming. She specialises in babies and does a package to include mum too.'
Amelia, mum to Ivy

Libraries

Check out the website, *www.surreycc.gov.uk/people-and-community/libraries*, for information on all of Surrey's libraries. Not only are libraries great for introducing your little ones to books, but they tend to run a range of children's activities and also have information on events running in the local area.

Guildford Library
77 North Street, GU1 4AL
0300 200 1001
www.surreycc.gov.uk/people-and-community/libraries
(Also see page 122 and *Bounce and Rhyme on pages 79 and 108*)

'You can get loads of information from *Guildford Library* and pick up a free bag with a couple of books and information on helping your child to read produced by Bookstart. Your child can have their own library card and take out nine books and they also hold a couple of free activity sessions per week including story telling. Get there early though as places fill up very quickly. There is a small lift to access all floors although the children's area is up the ramp from reception.'
Claire, mum to Orson

Libraries are not just for books ...

Local Sling Libraries
www.ukslinglibraries.wordpress.com

'Since my little girl was born, I've really enjoyed 'babywearing' (i.e. carrying her in a sling). I really like the freedom of being able to get around without a buggy, particularly for going on walks in the countryside and getting on and off buses and trains. It's also useful to be 'hands-free' if she wants to be carried and I need to get on with something at the same time.
It can be hard to find the right sling, particularly for an older baby, but you can borrow slings and find out more about the best and safest way to wear your baby at two local sling libraries (and meet lots of friendly babywearing mums!). I've been to the Farnham one (which has met in Guildford once and might do again).
There's also a new sling library for Surrey and Hants which meets in Godalming.'
Bronwen, mum to Olwen

Nappies

Babies and toddlers get through hundreds of nappies a year so it's important that

SERVICES

the choice of nappy is one that parents feel comfortable with. There are plenty of options available: disposable, eco disposable and washable. Many shops stock a range of disposable nappies and a quick internet search will reveal lots of stockists of ecos. With both of these it is usually a case of shopping around until you find a brand that suits. The decision to use washable nappies, however, can be a bit more daunting so we have included some experiences of local parents who give their reasons for choosing washable nappies, where to go to get started and some suggestions of where to buy them.

Why use washable nappies?

'There are lots of reasons to try washable nappies and we're really pleased we gave them a shot. We'd heard all the concerns about leakage, washing, smells and so on, but because we both loathe waste and landfill, we were keen to try. In the end, we've found washable nappies to be absolutely perfect for our needs, with no landfill waste (the liners are flushed away down the loo) and easier on our pockets too. We were lucky enough to be given our *Bambino Mio* nappies by a generous friend, who has already used them on her three children, but even after Alexander, they're still as good as new and work perfectly. The costs are mainly upfront rather than spread out, and there are ongoing washing costs, but even if we had bought them, we would still have made a significant saving as opposed to using disposables. Having said that, this cost point comes with a warning … the designs are so cute that you might find yourself obsessively shopping for gorgeous new nappies!!

As for the concerns, Alexander hasn't had any nappy rash since week three when we moved to washables (he spent the first three weeks in disposables as we had heard the concerns and were keen to get to grips with having a baby and moving house before trying something new – in fact we wish we'd used them from day one). Apart from the terra-poos which would have tested any nappy, we haven't suffered any leakage, and we confidently use washables even at night, when we simply put a waterproof wrap over the top. Even the wettest nappy doesn't leak through *Mother-ease* Rikki wraps.

The washing isn't really an issue. I don't find that putting a load in the machine takes any longer than taking bagfuls of dirty nappies to the outside bin, and there are so many different styles of nappies available that your drying facilities will be catered for. We don't have a tumble dryer but have a washing line. But for rainy days, we invested in an energy-efficient heated airer from Lakeland, which dries a whole load overnight. Although we haven't had to use it too much yet I can see it will be invaluable in the winter, and will be used for all our washing, not just the nappies. If like us you don't have a tumble dryer, I would recommend pre-fold nappies where the inner nappy comes away from the outer wrap, as they dry quicker. I know people complain about the environmental impact of washing but if you think carefully about your washing and drying, you can minimise this, and the effects of landfill were, for us, a key consideration.

As for the supposed dirty nappy smell, we simply use a lidded bucket to hold the dirty nappies, to which I add a few drops of lavender oil and tea tree oil, and as well as creating a pleasant smell (people have actually commented on the nice smell in Alexander's room!) the tea tree has antiseptic properties.

We have also been delighted to find other benefits to washable nappies. As well as the reduced cost and the environmental benefits, Alexander's lack of nappy rash is, I'm sure, due in large part to the fact that he doesn't sit in a wet nappy for long, and that we control what chemicals are against his skin. As a final persuasion, washable nappy designs are SO much cuter than disposables, and I enjoy putting him in his 'London bus pants' for trips into town, his 'Giraffe pants' for bed and the gorgeous fluffy 'Rainbow pants' we have for sunny days. Much more fun!'
Suzie, mum to Alexander

Getting started with washable nappies

The Nappy Lady
Farnham, GU9 1HP
0845 652 6532
info@thenappylady.co.uk
www.thenappylady.co.uk
(Also see *The Nappy Lady* on page 173)

'We contacted Wendy before our baby was born, because we were keen to use washable nappies but had no idea which to use, and how to navigate our way round the huge range of options available. Wendy invited us to her house, for a free, no-obligation demo of many of the nappies on the market. The couple of hours we spent with her completely demystified the whole washable nappy question, and also gave us some handy tips as to other things we might need to consider.

Wendy really knows her stuff about the different options, having used washables on all her children. If you are considering using washable nappies, I would highly recommend contacting Wendy to find out more. She also holds one of the *Surrey County Council* trial kits, so if you're still not sure, you can have a free trial before committing a penny.'
Suzie, mum to Alexander

'Whatever you call them – real, reusable, cloth – I knew at the least I wanted to learn more about current alternatives to disposable nappies. I was by no means committed to using cloth nappies, but after reading what I could about the options available today, I felt compelled to seek out first-hand expertise. *The Nappy Lady*, Wendy Richards, was the perfect resource. She is extremely knowledgeable, and her enthusiastic and approachable nature made it easy to leave her home feeling fully conversant in all the available options in the world of cloth nappies. Wendy has a wide range of products to hand, ready to see, feel and examine up close, and she takes a real interest in each family's circumstances and preferences, helping them find the most suitable nappy solution for them. Although she is obviously selling a product she believes in, we never felt any pressure to buy. We are very happy with our cloth nappies, and if you are at all curious about alternatives to disposables, I would happily recommend you consult with *The Nappy Lady.'*

Erin, mum to Sean

Surrey County Council
www.goreal.org.uk/surrey

'Ever worried about the quantity of nappies you're sending to landfill, but don't know where to start when it comes to re-useable nappies? *Surrey County Council* have a great scheme which allows you to borrow a trial pack of cloth nappies. The pack includes samples of all sorts of different nappies so that you can try them out on your baby before you make a decision about whether and what sort to use. You can also get a free info pack and DVD.

Check out the website to find out how to get hold of a trial pack (in Guildford the packs are based at *The Spinney* and the Hazel Avenue/York Road *Children's Centres* (see pages 162 and 164)).'

Bronwen, mum to Olwen

Where to buy washable nappies

Here are just a few suggestions. An internet search will come up with many more.

BabyCentre
www.babycentre.co.uk

Cloth Nappy Tree
www.clothnappytree.co.uk

The Used Nappy Company
www.usednappies.co.uk

'If you've decided to use cloth nappies but are finding the up-front cost a bit much (or just want to cut down environmental impact even more), you can pick up 'preloved' nappies online. The ones I've got have been in really good condition and

at a fraction of the price of new ones. Good places to start are *The Used Nappy Company* which is a sort of eBay for nappies, *Cloth Nappy Tree,* or there's a forum for buying and selling nappies in the community section of *BabyCentre.'*
Bronwen, mum to Olwen

Bambino Mio
www.uk.bambinomio.com/uk

'These are a really simple type of prefold nappy, with a *Mionappy* folded inside a *Miosoft* (the cover, done up with Velcro). We also use Mothercare nappy liners to wick moisture away from baby's skin and collect the worst of the poo. This is simply flushed down the loo. We find *Bambino Mio* nappies a little bulkier than disposables but have bought a few vest extenders from *The Nappy Lady* to combat this. And he simply goes into his bigger clothes a little earlier than he would otherwise have done! We are delighted with these in terms of design, leakage, comfort, washability and cost and would heartily recommend them.'
Suzie, mum to Alexander

Mother-ease
www.mother-ease.com

'The *Mother-ease* Rikki Wrap makes using washable nappies overnight a breeze. It's a wrap which simply Velcros over any other existing nappy and thanks to its slim size, doesn't make baby's bottom any bulkier than it needs to be. They come in a lovely range of colours and designs, and have a 'skirt' built in to prevent leakage. They wash beautifully and are really durable. One of ours has now been used on four children and still looks exactly the same as the new larger one I received today.'
Suzie, mum to Alexander

Nappies by Minki
www.minkinappies.co.uk

'We have a number of *Minki* Pocket nappies and I love them! I love the cute designs of sheep and rainbows (and I am about to order the Mini Monster with felt spikes along the baby's bottom) and I love the fact that the soft fleece sits snugly and comfortably against baby's skin, keeping him warm and cosy even when soiled. These are the comfiest and softest nappies I have found and although they look bulkier than some others, I haven't found clothes a problem with these and the cuteness of his big fleecy bottom more than makes up for any extra bulk!'
Suzie, mum to Alexander

The Nappy Lady
Farnham, GU9 1HP
0845 652 6532
info@thenappylady.co.uk
www.thenappylady.co.uk
(Also see *The Nappy Lady* on page 169)

'Wendy sells a huge range of washables through her website. On comparing her prices to other specialist and non-specialist websites and shops, we found her prices to be really competitive, and we also really love her Facebook page which allows followers to ask questions and be updated on discounts and new stock as they come up.'
Suzie, mum to Alexander

Naturebotts
www.naturebotts.co.uk

'*Naturebotts* is a friendly and efficient company with a smallish, but excellent range of eco-friendly products. I have bought all my children's nappies from here. You can arrange for them to send you a reminder email when you might be running out (invaluable for me and my sieve brain), there are discounts if you buy in bulk and delivery is super speedy.'
Katie, mum to Beth and Asa

Tots Bots
www.totsbots.com

'I bought a *Tots Bots* EasyFit nappy to try, as I really love their designs. It's an all-in-one nappy, where the booster is inserted inside a pocket on the wrap, so making them quick to dry when pulled apart. Although I am really happy with this nappy and it washes beautifully time and time again, my only reason for not buying more is that each time baby wets his nappy, the whole thing has to be washed, as opposed to the *Bambino Mio* brand where only the folded nappy is washed and the cover can be used until soiled. But *Tots Bots* definitely have some of the cutest designs on the market for your baby's bottom!'
Suzie, mum to Alexander

Websites

We hope this book has been useful in providing ideas for things do with your children, but in case you need some more inspiration, here are a few websites for what's on in Guildford and the surrounding area.

Day Out With the Kids
www.dayoutwiththekids.co.uk/things-to-do/guildford

'This is a national website and so also very useful for finding things to do while on holiday in the UK. We discovered a fantastic soft play area using this site that we wouldn't have found otherwise, which was a lifesaver when we needed something to do on a couple of very rainy days on holiday.'
Gemma, mum to Daniel

Ideas for the Kids
www.ideasforthekids.co.uk

'Another national website. Just put in your postcode and it will give you a list of ideas.'
Gemma, mum to Daniel

The Guide 2 Surrey
www.theguide2surrey.com

Hopscotch
www.hopscotch-online.com

Surrey Family Information Service
eycscomms.newsweaver.com/Parentspage

Surrey Mummy
www.surreymummy.com

'I find them all really useful for things to do, original ideas and finding out what's going on.'
Claire, mum to Orson

Acknowledgements

We would like to say a huge thank you to the following people:

All the parents, grandparents and other family members (and of course their babies, toddlers and pre-schoolers) who wrote reviews. The reviews truly are the stars of the show.

All the advertisers whose adverts funded the printing of this book. If you contact them, don't forget to mention where you saw their ad.

The chapter editors, Ellie Atkins, Alistair Gerrard, Katie Kelly, Tracy Liennard, Susan Sanderson (also back cover blurb) and Claire West, who did a wonderful job of collecting and collating reviews.

Suzie Maine, for proofreading and her patient guidance on editing matters, general book production process and for putting up with our endless stream of questions! Also for liaising with the typesetter and printers.

Victoria Speirs for imparting her words of wisdom and vast knowledge of the second edition and all things book-related.

Everyone on the Guildford NCT committee who helped out. Particularly Katie Kelly for getting the ball rolling, Shelley Collinson for all her help and support, and also Claire Hares for her advertising contacts and pointing us in the right direction on the advertising process.

Earnest (*earnest-agency.com*) for the cover design.

Nigel Mitchell at Shore Books and Design for book design and typesetting.

Kate Inskip for indexing.

ACKNOWLEDGEMENTS

Our husbands, Warren Applegate and Stephen Gregson, for their support and putting up with the many hours we spent co-ordinating this project, meeting with those who helped us, writing reviews and chapters, encouraging others to write reviews, managing the financials, editing, contacting advertisers and promoting this book.

Our sons, Ellis Applegate and Daniel Gregson, for introducing us to the baby and toddler world of Guildford and for whom we hope this book will be the source of many a fun day out.

Anyone else who assisted us in any way. We are extremely grateful for all the information and ideas we have received.

And finally, you, the readers, for buying this book.

We do hope you enjoy reading this new edition of *Tots About Town* and visiting the places in it as much as we have enjoyed producing it.

Best Wishes

Carla Applegate and Gemma Gregson

Index

INDEX

INDEX

INDEX

INDEX

INDEX

INDEX